Good Medicine

Cliffelk Press

To Gladys —
Best wishes — your son
Jim made our dream
a reality — Tom Clifford

Good Medicine

How Wit and Guile
Saved the School of Medicine
at the University of North Dakota

Tom Clifford
Robert Eelkema, MD
and Patrick A. McGuire

FIRST EDITION

Cliffelk Press
Grand Forks, North Dakota

Good Medicine: How Wit and Guile Saved the School of Medicine at the University of North Dakota by Tom Clifford; Robert Eelkema, MD; and Patrick A. McGuire.

Published 2004 by Cliffelk Press, Grand Forks, North Dakota. Cliffelk Press is not a division, department, or subsidiary of the University of North Dakota. For ordering information, please email: pat.mcguire@comcast.net or call 410-996-8900.

Edited by Richard Conway and Richard H. Johnson

Cover and Interior Book Design by Pneuma Books, LLC
For more info, visit www. pneumabooks.com

Type set in Berling Roman 10.^{75} / 14.^{75}. Titling set in Ex Ponto & Frutiger Roman.

FIRST EDITION ~ FIRST PRINTING

This book is printed on acid-free archival paper and features a Smythe Sewn Library Binding.

Printed in the United States of America by Thomson Shore, Dexter Michigan.

08 07 06 05 04 03   6 5 4 3 2 1

Publisher's Cataloging-In-Publication
(*Provided by Quality Books, Inc.*)

Clifford, Thomas J. (Thomas John), 1921-
    Good medicine : how wit and guile saved the School of
Medicine at the University of North Dakota / Tom
Clifford, Robert Eelkema and Patrick A. McGuire. --
1st ed.
    p. cm.
    Includes bibliographical references and index.
    LCCN 2003108688
    ISBN 0-9743105-4-9

    1. University of North Dakota. School of Medicine--
History. 2. Medical colleges--North Dakota--Grand Forks
--History. I. Eelkema, Robert. II. McGuire, Patrick
A., 1946- III. Title.

R747.U68365C55 2003   610'.71'178416
                QBI03-200531

*This book is dedicated to the people of North Dakota
and in particular, for their loyalty and dedication,
to Jim Brosseau, Bud Shutt, Dick Smith and Sue Huus.*

Table *of* Contents

Preface

In January of 1971, the Board of Higher Education named me president of the University of North Dakota. I didn't officially assume my duties, however, until the first of July, which gave me time to survey the state of the university and to gear up for what I assumed would be the most challenging and urgent issues facing me. In looking here and there during those six months, I admit that I didn't do much more than cast a brief glance at our two-year medical school. It had a fine national reputation, our students ranked with top students across the country, and many went on to complete their four-year degree at prestigious medical colleges such as Harvard, Northwestern and Yale. It seemed to have plenty of funding and was run by capable people. I told myself that here was one area that wasn't going to be a problem.

I had barely taken office, however, when I was rudely awakened from my complacency. Capable medical school men like Wally Nelson, Willard Wright, John Vennes and Bobby Eelkema had been scrambling during those six months to find a way to deal with a shift in medical policy nationwide that was about to hit North Dakota like a spring storm.

Essentially, the medical schools that had once eagerly taken our two-year graduates as transfers into their third and fourth years of study were now telling us they didn't have room. In a handful of years there might well be no place to send our students, no matter how bright or brimming with potential they might be. At about the same time, the Carnegie Commission and others had called for an end to two-year medical schools. That meant, perhaps, shutting down our medical school. It also meant even fewer doctors in our already doctor-starved small communities across the state.

I had two immediate concerns. As a native North Dakotan I didn't like the idea of not having a medical school. I felt our kids should have the right to become doctors just like anybody else. And if they didn't have that opportunity, we were going to suffer even more in our small communities because the health care wouldn't be there.

But beyond all that, really, was the old-fashioned attitude of a guy from a small state saying, "Why can't we do it?" Sometimes, I think, we are too apologetic in North Dakota when it comes to whether we deserve or can produce things of the highest quality.

Sometimes we are too willing to settle for less than the best in order to have whatever it is we want, including doctors. There was a feeling in the 1970s that we couldn't have a four-year medical school in North Dakota because we didn't have what it took to turn out excellent doctors. Some thought we should just stick with the two-year school and see what happens — or close the medical school and take whatever foreign doctors we could attract to our rural state. But the group of visionaries I mentioned above knew exactly what would happen if we started down either of those two paths. Eventually, we'd end up with a lesser university, something we would long have cause to regret.

From the outset of our plan to make a four-year medical school happen, I felt that if we couldn't create a school that turned out the highest quality of doctors, then our plan wasn't worth doing. At the same time, I really believed we could build such a school. So did men like Nelson and Wright and Vennes and Eelkema. And, as it turned out, we did do it — to the utter amazement of more than one high-level naysayer who underestimated North Dakota grit and inventiveness.

Speaking of which, we didn't always do things the way they were supposed to be done or the way a lot of people expected them to be done. For better or worse, I have always been a bit of a maverick. Those who know me are aware that I chafe easily under the strictures of excessive talking about a problem — especially when the need for action seems so obvious and the path toward resolution so evident. So we cut corners, sometimes at blinding speed. And we got around red tape in many cases by simply ignoring it. Though these events took place only thirty years ago, those were different times. Now red tape has become thicker and nearly impossible to sidestep. Today's bureaucratic environment favors setting up a committee to consider the formation of a committee to look into establishing a committee to explore the value of creating a committee, pending, of course, approval of a special committee of the whole.

About a year ago, I bumped into a longtime friend, Dr. Bobby Eelkema. As we chatted, we began to recall the people who had helped us and some of the unusual methods we had used to surmount bureaucratic and legislative obstacles to our achievement of a four-year medical school. We knew that our close associate, Dr. John Vennes, was at the time preparing an exhaustive history of the medical school from its founding in 1905 through the present day. That volume is bound to be the definitive study of our school, prepared by an honorable man (who, nevertheless, knows where all the bodies are buried).

Bob and I, however, talked of a more focused story, a re-examination, if you will, as opposed to an unabridged history. We wanted to tell a story about what people can do in this state when they set their minds to it and are driven by a sense of purpose. The events from 1971 through 1973 that led to the establishment of a four-year medical school and several key residency programs were not the doing of one man — certainly not myself. The effort, in a way, was a dance we choreographed from moment to moment, a creative application of spirit and wit, inspired by the belief that North

Dakota not only deserved but desperately needed a high quality four-year medical school.

Keep in mind it had long been established that freshly minted doctors will settle down within 100 miles of where they get final residency training. When you send a student to Chicago to get that training, the odds are heavy that Chicago is where that student will practice. Put a full-fledged medical school in North Dakota and you immediately increase the likelihood of many more young doctors settling down in their home state to practice medicine.

That's exactly what has happened. But it didn't happen by accident, and Bob and I wanted to give credit to the heretofore largely unsung individuals who showed the courage, the creativity, and, most important, the energy to carry the project to completion. For there was a good deal of opposition to the idea of a four-year school. It took many voices to make converts. Along the way we needed certain approvals among doctors and legislators at state and local levels. Without this small cadre of volunteers, the project would, in all likelihood, have failed.

Who were these volunteers? What exactly did they do? That was the story Bob Eelkema and I talked about. The more we did, the more we realized it was a story we ourselves could not and should not attempt to tell. Each of us was too close to the daily action in those days to render an objective view. We decided to bring in a professional journalist, Pat McGuire, to sort through the records, talk to as many people as possible who remember those unusual days, and write an objective story.

For our medical school is an exceptional institution whose story deserves to be known. Consider that if you go into Montana, you'll find lots of specialists in Billings and Great Falls, but they have a heck of a time getting physicians in their small towns. Yet you can go into small towns in North Dakota, such as Rugby or Hettinger, and find robust medical centers staffed almost exclusively by graduates of the medical school at UND. These are good, solid humanistic doctors imbued with a sense of idealism and mission.

Today we are turning out as good a product as you could ask for — and we have every right to ask for such high quality. It's no secret that we have been proud of our outstanding doctors and our medical school. Now through this story, we hope to acknowledge the achievements of some extraordinary individuals who were there when they were needed. I'm proud of every one of them.

Tom Clifford
Grand Forks, 2003

$\mathcal{F}$oreword

Three or four times a week during the late 1950s when I was a young medical student at the University of North Dakota, I gravitated toward the old cement handball courts. One of my frequent and toughest opponents was the dean of the business school, Tom Clifford. He was an easy man to like, always self-effacing, compassionate toward students, and not without a sense of humor. He liked to tell the story about how he once helped an academically challenged football player write a term paper. A few days later, as Tom and some professors were walking across campus, the football player rushed up to him and shouted excitedly, "Dean, we got a C on our paper!" In spite of Tom's impressive credentials — a law degree, an MBA from Stanford, a UND degree in accounting — there were those on campus who held themselves above him. He was not what they considered a pure academic. The professors with him that day chuckled at the low grade his football player had received. But Tom, as was so typical of his steel and style, shot back, "That's proof that you professors have it in for athletes. That paper was absolutely worth a B."

Over the years, Tom and I built a strong friendship through our play on the courts and during the handball parties following various tournaments. I remember playing handball with him in late 1970 and early 1971 when I was chairman of the department of community medicine at the School of Medicine, and he was a dark horse candidate to become president of the university. It looked for a time as if the selection committee was going to hire someone outside North Dakota, someone with those very fine credentials that academics seem to prize so blindly. It angered me that anyone could pass over such a capable and intelligent man like Tom Clifford. Of course, they didn't — or, rather, they tried but failed.

It then became my great pleasure not only to have my friend become president, but to be able to serve him almost immediately. For the future of our medical school suddenly was cast into doubt. This book tells the story of how Tom Clifford and a handful of loyal associates not only saved the medical school, but expanded it into a unique, degree-granting, four-year school with innovative residency programs geared to the kind of primary care most needed by citizens of our state.

Tom was never a man given to undue formality. So it was that he and a handpicked group of strategists — myself included — would meet once a week at a corner table of the Chuck House in the Westward Ho Motor Inn for breakfast, where we summarized our progress and plotted our next moves. There were no grand committees named to study this question. Tom has always been a man of action and so we acted. With the wisdom and energy of men like John Vennes, Willard Wright and Wally Nelson, we accomplished some amazing things in a very short time.

Now that our medical school is so successful and recognized across the country as a model in the training of community-oriented doctors, it's easy to forget the work carried out thirty years ago that made it all happen. But that work should not be forgotten, nor should the names of those men and women who came together from opposing sides of the political aisle to accomplish something that would benefit all. I'm thinking of doctors such as Phil Dahl and Richard Johnson and George Johnson and Grandon Tolstedt and Dean Strinden; of legislators such as the late Brynhild Haugland of Minot and Oscar Solberg of Rolla and those we still have with us, including Bryce Streibel and Earl Strinden and Evan Lips. They are among the cadre of the unsung, whose efforts during this movement were invaluable.

When Tom and I started talking recently about writing a history of this movement to capture the excitement and import of those days, I happened to meet a journalist named Patrick McGuire. Pat was once a reporter at *The Denver Post* where he'd befriended a North Dakotan colleague named Rykken Johnson. Rykken is a UND grad who had divided his time during his undergraduate days writing for the student newspaper and playing varsity baseball. As is proper for any North Dakota son, he waxed eloquently and frequently to Pat about the positives of his home state — and particularly of his hometown of Drayton. He did such a fine job that Pat has visited Drayton often with Rykken, even writing a long and glowing piece in *The Denver Post* about the town and state some years back. A singer and banjo player, Pat has even written a song about North Dakota, "Where the Red River Flows."

As it happens, Drayton is where my family settled when we moved from Minnesota in my teen years. I knew Rykken then as Richard Johnson, the all-star baseball playing son of Chaud Johnson, who ran the Drayton State Bank. In fact, once during the 1970s, Dr. Jim Brosseau and I visited Denver and met with Richard — he had by then adopted his grandfather's surname Rykken — at the Denver Press Club. I talked to him about the MEDEX program I had started at UND — an innovative training program that trained returning corpsmen from the Vietnam War as physician assistants to supplement medical coverage in rural areas across the country.

Richard, at that time a reporter with the *Rocky Mountain News*, wrote a piece about the program. It was natural, then, that I would look him up when Tom Clifford and I agreed we should take the bull by the horns and find a writer to help us with our project. Richard, who is today an editor in the communications office of the Denver Water Department, immediately recommended his old friend Pat McGuire for the job. Pat spent twenty-seven years as a reporter with

The Post and *The Baltimore Sun,* winning several national awards and being nominated three times by his editors for a Pulitzer Prize. He has taught journalism at several schools, including the University of Maryland.

I flew to Baltimore where Pat now works as a freelance writer, editor and writing coach. We hit it off, so we then met with Tom and we all agreed to get going. In the course of his research, Pat has traveled about 3,000 miles across North Dakota, tracking down doctors and legislators who played key roles in the early 1970s in getting the four-year medical program going. But he also stopped off at various clinics and doctors' offices in places like New Town, Hettinger and Williston to interview graduates of the UND medical school. His profiles of those physicians, which make up the second part of this book, are the best proof of all that what was accomplished was a most worthy goal.

Robert Eelkema, M.D.
Grand Forks, 2003

Introduction

Perhaps the real question here is whether or not an account of how the two-year medical school at the University of North Dakota reinvented itself into a four-year school thirty years ago is a story at all. It sounds more like a tinder dry report, one of those wheezy bureaucratic garblings that make the eyes glaze over. Not exactly *War and Peace*. And in the end, who really cares about bureaucratic shell games played so long ago? Surely, most of those who would care have long since shuffled off to Buffalo.

That's a fair reaction — in fact, it was my reaction when I was approached by Bob Eelkema and Tom Clifford about reassembling all the salient details of this old paper chase into a coherent and readable story. But it took only one afternoon with the spirited, anecdote-rich Dr. Eelkema, and one pleasant evening under the Hibernian spell of Tom Clifford's twinkling understatement for the weight of the story to sink in. It went way beyond a mere report of outflanking legislative committees and outfoxing ponderous politicians. This was a genuine story chock-full of cowboys, Indians, gamblers, fakers, Marines and handball players. It was packed full, not just of people *but of characters*: rounded individuals full of contradictions, beset by flaws and bolstered by inner strengths. In other words, the kind of mavericks that North Dakota grows with pride and nurtures so well.

Consider: There's a pilot in this story who is flying some key people from North Dakota to Washington, D.C., at a particularly critical moment, and he gets lost. But using common sense instilled by his North Dakota rearing, he drops down out of the sky to rooftop level and follows some recognizable Washington landmarks to the airport. The FAA later raises holy hell and says this isn't at all the way we do it back here. But no matter. The mission is accomplished and there is lots of chuckling up in Grand Forks.

There's a wild young boy in this story who shoots the neighbor's cat from a bedroom window. The neighbor later rewards him to the tune of $575,000.

There's a wily old man who does nothing more than build a swimming pool without anyone's permission. Perhaps if he hadn't, the highly regarded medical school might not exist today.

There's a doctor who has a gift for securing federal grants and an even greater gift for his creative disbursements of those monies. Such creativity today might earn him a vacation in a place like Leavenworth. Back then it ultimately earned medical degrees for deserving young men and women of North Dakota.

In this story there's a man known by some as "a crooked son of a bitch" whose bluster and bluff, nevertheless, carried many a day. There's a man called Moses. There's a very excellent fistfight scene. Even a dish called Finn and Haddie plays a role along with numerous instances of outrageous fibs and truth stretchings, of arm twistings and pressure points skillfully pressed.

The characters in this story are three-dimensional and human enough to lapse into the occasional night of drinking or blackjack or both. Most display equal parts of courage, wit and ruthlessness. Always they are driven by the righteousness of their mission.

Ultimately, this is the story of a very well thought-out end run around the pompous, bean-counting establishment that stands in the way of progress for the sake of i-dotting and t-crossing.

Yet it happened so fast, the question remains today: did anyone see it? Does anyone really appreciate the happy mincemeat that was made of rules and decorum in accomplishing this most worthy goal?

The answer: probably not. Which is why on one level this does remain a dusty, bloodless report of votes cast and bills ratified. But not too far beneath the surface, it's basically a story about people, about characters, about a leadership style whose time has probably, and regretfully, passed.

This book is divided in two parts. The first half, "A Marvelous Medical Adventure," borrows its title from a favorite phrase of Dr. George Magnus Johnson, a mainstay of the pediatric department at the School of Medicine for more than thirty years. Dr. Johnson is one of the true role players in this story of how a bold and clever university president led an unlikely assemblage of doctors, educators and legislators in a battle against political hardheads, ultimately guaranteeing North Dakotans a higher level of health care. Armed only with the purity of altruism and the ruthlessness of guile, their quest was certainly marvelous.

The second half, "Good Medicine," is a title inspired by the Hidatsa name given to Dr. Monica Mayer, a Native American graduate of the UND School of Medicine, now practicing in New Town. The inspiring story of her selfless dedication to the people on the Fort Berthold Reservation where she grew up, is precisely what Tom Clifford and Bob Eelkema had in mind when they envisioned a modern, degree-granting medical school that would address the real health care needs of rural North Dakota. In this half of the book, in the stories of UND doctors such as Monica Mayer, comes the ultimate proof that not only were the unusual strategies employed to effect the expansion of the medical school justified, but that they came none too soon.

Patrick A. McGuire
Abingdon, Maryland, 2003

"For they live, not in the urban world with its lonely crowd, but on the prairie, where the sparsity of population emphasizes the worth of the individual, where each is needed and each can do his part in the upward struggle of a rural society."

— *Elwyn Robinson,*
History of North Dakota

"Why would someone like me spend all these years obtaining these skills and go to the big city and take care of people who I don't know, probably never will know and probably don't care that much about? It seems to make better sense to take those skills and come home and take care of people who really need it and you don't have to teach yourself to care. You just do it naturally. I think that makes for better medicine."

— *Monica Mayer, M.D.*

PART ONE

A Marvelous Medical Adventure

The Handwriting on the Wall

1

Most of the action in this story takes place over a two-year period from 1971 through 1973. To fully appreciate the events of those two years, however, one needs first the context of the previous hundred.

Before 1870, the only doctors in what was then the Dakota Territory were Army officers stationed at posts such as Fort Union or Fort Abraham Lincoln. Some were assigned to detachments of troops that accompanied wagon trains heading to the Pacific Coast. By 1872 the Northern Pacific Railroad crossed the Red River, bringing with it an army of navvies and engineers and a handful of company doctors. Already a hearty band of Bohemian squatters had set up an informal tent encampment near what would soon be the city of Fargo.

According to Harley French, perhaps the greatest dean the School of Medicine has ever had, the first non-military doctor in the territory was a Northern Pacific employee named Kurtz in 1871. But he moved on when the railroad did. The population in the Territory in those days was less than 3,000, yet within three years Fargo was a city. In 1878 a newly arrived Fargo man, Dr. E.M. Darrow, had begun accepting patients. By 1884 Fargo could boast fourteen doctors. Meanwhile, up the river in Grand Forks, a similar story was unfolding, this at the hands of the Great Northern Railway. By the time North Dakota was admitted to the Union in 1889, the state numbered more than 182,000 souls, about 200 of them doctors.

These were days before rigid national standards were in place for the training of doctors. Private medical schools — many known as "wildcat schools" — unaffiliated with any hospitals or universities, provided about ten months of widely varying education. For the graduates, this was usually followed by two years as an apprentice of sorts under the guidance of a medical preceptor. According to French, the chief diagnostic instruments of these early horse-and-buggy doctors were the stethoscope and clinical thermometer. Diagnosis was crude and limited. Doctors knew simple means of determining sugar and albumin in urine, but there were no x-rays or basic diagnostic tests, and nothing like the lab work of modern times.

The chief medical concerns of the day were outbreaks of killer diseases such as diphtheria and typhoid. In one notable epidemic in Grand Forks in 1892, nearly 500 people fell ill with typhoid and 150 died. It was discovered that the town of Crookston, Minnesota, had been dumping its raw sewage into the Red Lake River, a tributary that flows into the Red River at Grand Forks.

Enterprisingly, two professors from the fledgling University of North Dakota applied themselves to resolving the problem. They helped design and supervise a slow sand filter that cleaned up the city's water and ended typhoid outbreaks. One of those men was Melvin A. Brannon, a professor of biology who would eventually push for the creation of a medical school at the University of North Dakota and become its first dean.

Five years before, in 1887, the territorial legislature had set aside $1,000 for a medical college at the university. But almost immediately, the chief proponent of the school left the university — which consisted then of a single building.

Brannon, a master organizer, revived the medical school idea during the late 1890s and into the first years of the twentieth century. He developed a strategy that curiously foreshadowed the efforts of another gifted organizer, Tom Clifford. When he set out in 1971 to expand the medical school, he used much the same tactics that had succeeded for Brannon. For in order to get the medical school open in the first place, Brannon went to work on two groups whose support was crucial for such an enterprise: legislators and doctors. His subtle tactics of persuasion eventually succeeded in starting the school and keeping it funded. He simply noted that young men and women who wanted to become doctors were leaving the state for their training and not coming back.

As the last century dawned, that argument struck a responsive chord among legislators, most of whom were farmers living in rural settings with little or no access to medical care. At the same time there was a movement in the medical world to formalize and standardize medical education. A period of forty-five months was prescribed for such training. To separate the "wildcat" proprietary medical schools from the legitimate, some began affiliating with major universities. Even smaller colleges could take part by providing laboratory courses and basic science courses that were to be taught in the first two years of a doctor's training.

"It might be wondered," wrote Harley French some years later, "if the university might not better have kept out of the field of medical education. [But] the writer ... is convinced that scientific medicine is so important to all of the people, that most of the state universities should undertake to do their share by offering instruction and research in the laboratory sciences at least."

Headed precisely in that direction, UND opened its school of pharmacy in 1902, which began working up a pre-medical curriculum. Prodded by Brannon, the faculty voted in 1905 to establish a two-year, basic sciences program. Legislative approval soon followed and UND became one of ten "half-schools" of medicine created in the first decade of the twentieth century. The "half-schools" were more or less feeder schools to the larger four-year institutions that had established themselves and emphasized clinical training.

The two-year medical school in Grand Forks accepted its first students in 1907 and awarded its first "certificate in medicine" in 1909 to Dr. Sverre Oftedal. He went on to practice in Fargo. That same year, Abraham Flexner, a high school principal from Louisville, Kentucky, began visiting many of the nation's 166 medical schools. Flexner had earlier written a critique of American colleges that considerably impressed the Carnegie Foundation. The foundation hired him to do a similar critique of American and Canadian medical schools. The reason: doubts had been raised by the American Medical Association as to the large number of proprietary medical schools still operating, and the quality of their graduates.

Flexner is viewed today as a muckraker, part of the Progressive Era's tough-minded reform movement that included Upton Sinclair, Lincoln Steffens and Ida Tarbell. Curiously, Flexner had never before been to a medical school other than the renowned school of medicine at The Johns Hopkins University in Baltimore. Flexner had earned his undergraduate degree at Hopkins and, using its medical school as his yardstick, severely criticized those schools, small and large, that he felt did not measure up to it. The report he produced after his year of investigation faulted dozens of schools, especially smaller schools and privately run schools, whose basic science curriculum he found lacking. His report was the first to set out rigid standards for medical education, research and the licensing of doctors.

One can only imagine the trepidation with which UND officials welcomed Flexner to the campus in 1909. They needn't have worried, for the great reformer had nothing but praise for the still evolving medical school with its tiny annual budget of $6,500. He was impressed, he said, by the sound teaching principles he had observed at UND. North Dakota, he wrote, "though thinly settled, is prosperous and no anxiety is felt that the high standard will deplete the medical profession of the state."

A year later, the unassuming Harley E. French arrived as the new dean — perhaps the most significant hiring in the history of the UND School of Medicine. A graduate of Northwestern, French had held the deanship at the University of South Dakota, another of the states that had formed two-year medical schools. Upon arrival in Grand Forks, French said he "found small but possible quarters assigned the school in Old Science Hall, with laboratories and class rooms in proportion. Laboratory equipment and library showed intelligent and thoughtful care. There was a small but good faculty, and there were about a dozen medical students, and perhaps twenty students in the premedical years. In short, the school was a going concern."

He kept it going for nearly forty years, often through the sheer force of his own will. He wore every imaginable hat from dean of admissions, to professor, to head of the curriculum committee. He was not without his idiosyncrasies. According to John Vennes, who decades later headed the same curriculum committee, French chewed snuff and even kept a spot of sand in his desk drawer where he could spit.

"He had not only a well-trained mind but a classical education and was possessed of tireless energy and absolute integrity," recalled Theodore Harwood, a future dean of the school. But mostly, says Vennes, "he was known as a taskmaster: either you learned gross anatomy or you didn't survive."

French needed to be tough, for he faced some awfully tough times, especially during the Great Depression. The school's budget fell impossibly low and national accrediting bodies were much more skeptical than Flexner about whether the school could go on.

"For years Dr. French patiently presented the needs of the school to the people and the legislature," recalled Harwood, "and since the state was always without the income, his requests were turned down."

During the Depression the state's income dropped from $315 million to $111 million annually. A third of all farmers lost their farms. A third of taxes were delinquent by 1937. The salary for deans at UND was cut from $4,800 to $1,920. Facing drastic cuts in state appropriations, the medical school struggled on, although in 1936 it was dropped from membership by the Association of American Medical Colleges.

In fact, the AAMC's Council on Medical Education declared, "The University of North Dakota does not have what can be called a medical school." And yet, wrote Harwood, despite the lack of space, budget, books and equipment, the school maintained its average enrollment of about thirty students a year, and graduated 142 in a five-year period in the heart of the Great Depression.

"Their mistake," wrote Harwood of the AAMC, "was in trying to measure teaching by measuring floor space, gauging teaching by faculty publications, estimating teaching ability by the number of degrees and the salary paid to the members of the faculty and evaluating the library by the number of books, not those read. The survey committee could not measure and did not appreciate the virtuosity of a small group of dedicated teachers and students who knew that they could not coast into an education."

Even so, it becomes clear in reading French's articles written during the 1930s that discouragement was a daily adversary.

"Unlike many of the medical schools of the country, North Dakota has not shared in the generous, almost extravagant expenditures for buildings and equipment that have been so common," he said. "It is one of the schools that has had to carry on with very modest provisions in every way. Its support has been from the state which has had many calls for every dollar it had to spend...

"What of the future of the school? Will there continue to be a place for any two-year school? Will it ever be a complete school?"

This was the first public acknowledgment of the hopes of many that North Dakota's "half school" would one day become a full-fledged, four-year, degree-granting institution. But speaking from the heart of Midwestern darkness in 1936, French wrote, "So far as we can now foresee the future, the state should not look forward to having a complete medical school. Possibly the work of the first two years, well provided for, is the reasonable share to expect from a state of the wealth, population and social conditions of North Dakota."

In so stating, French voiced the argument that was to provide so much fuel for the opposition in later decades when the four-year idea was revived.

"Even if the state were able," he said, "there would most likely be an inadequate amount of clinical material in several important branches: obstetrics, emergency services, acute infectious diseases." Wealthy, populous cities like Chicago, he noted, "not only will have an abundance of clinical material but the hospitals. Possibly this is sour grapes since the prospect for a complete school are no nearer now than they were twenty years ago. It simply means that the problem is difficult at best."

French continued to argue in Bismarck for more funding. Rejected again and again, he managed to keep the school together through determination and stubbornness, even canceling subscriptions to professional medical journals to save a few dollars. Finally in 1945, as the nation emerged from war, and prosperity seemed just around the corner, the State Legislature heard his pleas.

It appropriated $250,000 for a new building to house the medical school. French, who would retire two years later, had one more victory coming. The 1947 session of the legislature agreed to put up for public vote in the general election a measure that would authorize a one-mill levy on taxable property in the state. The proceeds would go straight to the School of Medicine. It was the first and only levy for any specific program in state history. The rationale was clear: a properly funded medical school, one that would eventually expand to a degree-granting school, would guarantee the state more doctors. As though to bear out the old saying that North Dakotans are worried about two things, the weather and their health, the measure easily passed.

The School of Medicine now was on a roll. In the fall 1949 issue of the regional medical journal *Lancet*, a University of Kansas professor wrote a glowing review of UND's medical school and spoke enthusiastically about the likelihood of its growing into a four-year program. A year later, the American Medical Association following up on that idea, sent a team to Grand Forks to inspect the medical school. Their report suggested that the university seriously consider a plan to add the third and fourth years of study and to begin granting medical degrees.

The university's medical center advisory committee — created to administer the mill levy — then recruited a blue-ribbon panel to formulate such a plan. Two men it had in mind for the panel were John Ascott, dean of the medical school at the University of Alberta, and William E. Brown, dean at the University of Vermont's medical college. Both oversaw the type of regional, four-year medical school that the advisory committee envisioned for North Dakota.

As it turned out, Brown couldn't make it and sent in his place Dr. Theodore H. Harwood. Abruptly, all glowing talk of a four-year school hit a bump. Ascott and Harwood suggested a new curriculum be written for the medical school before expansion be seriously considered.

But the idea of a four-year school wouldn't go away. In 1953, the State Legislature took the unusual step of passing a bill that directed the creation of a four-year medical school. It backed that up with a revision of the mill-levy authorization, decreeing that "a sufficient portion of such funds ... shall be retained by the Board of Higher Education to permit the establishment of a third year course of medicine at the center not later than 1955 and a fourth year course not later than 1956 ... "

With that timetable in mind, the board then hired Dr. Harwood away from Vermont to be the new dean of the medical school, and to carry out that four-year vision. His hiring made sense because Vermont, after all, was a state whose two-year medical school had expanded to four years. But what no one seemed to grasp at the time was that Harwood had no intention of expanding the school to four years, in spite of the sentiment behind the mill levy. In fact, he would essentially bury the idea for the next eighteen years, convinced like French before him that the state was just too small to provide a medical school with enough patients for training. By 1957, the year the legislature had envisioned the medical school would add its fourth year, talk of the expansion had almost completely died out.

A decade later, the North Dakota Legislature got a rude awakening. For several years, the proceeds from the one-mill levy had been more than enough to cover the costs of running the School of Medicine. Harwood was even able to get a rehabilitation hospital built in Grand Forks. But by 1967, expenses had outgrown the levy, and the medical center advisory committee had to ask the state for additional funds. Those monies were granted, but the prospect of new expenses did not go down well with cost-conscious legislators.

For in spite of earlier support for a four-year school, there were now quite a few legislators opposed to any medical school at all. They based their objections on a pure cost-to-benefit ratio. It took millions now to graduate about sixty medical students a year, compared to the much lower per-capita rate for the thousands of students graduating annually from the state's other colleges and universities. Such bang-for-the-buck grumbling continued through 1971, a year when the mill levy brought in $1.4 million to the medical school, but the legislature was forced to come up with another $1.2 million.

"Back in those days it was quite a bit of money," recalls C. Emerson Murray, the gravel voiced lawyer from Rugby. In those days, he ran the Legislative Council, the research arm of the State Legislature. "They got that appropriation with a certain amount of reluctance. There were a majority of negative comments. They were doubtful they wanted to take on that kind of long-term financial commitment. Legislators are pessimistic on revenue forecasts always. And back in those days they were especially pessimistic."

Meanwhile, Murray recalls, there was talk that UND was again looking at creating a four-year medical school.

"I think most legislators thought they wanted more medical services and more coverage in the state, so there was that desire," he says today. "It was the usual desire in the legislature to be pro-education and provide opportunities to young people, even though an awful lot of them go on and make their fortune elsewhere. But the legislature had not assigned this four-year school idea to the Legislative Council as a study area or a policy determination project. That went to their reluctance and a bit of negativism. So I would have to say the prospects in 1971 were not really especially bright. Not even 50–50. A full-blown medical school didn't seem in the offing."

Meanwhile, during the late 1960s and early 1970s, political forces had reached critical mass. Complaints were common across the land: people could not find a doctor at a reasonable price to take care of them. Some suggested that the problem was a lack of medical students going into primary care. The federal government was putting too much money into research, said some critics, and not enough into training doctors who could actually handle the primary care of the everyday sick.

Specialists seemed to rule the day. More and more medical students went into specialties and sub-specialties; general practitioners began leaving the field to become specialists because that's where the money was. Medicare and other government programs just didn't reimburse as well for primary care as it did for specialized care.

For one reason or another, it was clear to the public that there just weren't enough physicians to go around.

One man who understood the problem quite well — and later served as a valued consultant to the UND School of Medicine — was Dr. Bill Harlan. A former dean at the medical schools of Duke University and the University of Alabama, Harlan remembers the argument in 1970 that the supply and demand situation could be rectified only by creating more primary-care practitioners.

"The government had been saying we're going to see that Medicare and other government programs reimburse better for primary care than for specialty care," he says. "Of course, it didn't occur. But that was one idea. Another was the notion that we needed more doctors. And the reason that the public perceived the cost so great was because there were a small number of doctors who saw patients for a limited amount of time and charged too much money. There was a feeling that if we had more doctors, we'd do better. That was particularly true in rural areas. If you looked at North Dakota then, you would have seen a very large number of people per physician."

In fact, a 1970 report showed that North Dakota had a ratio of only eighty-four doctors per 100,000 people — barely half the national rate. Of those doctors, a third were graduates of the two-year medical school in Grand Forks. They were once students who had gone on from North Dakota to get their medical degrees and their residency training but had come back. Many, though, were concentrated in Fargo, Grand Forks and Bismarck, and many were also in late middle age, approaching retirement.

The sense of national urgency about the need for more doctors reached its peak in 1970 with the release of a report on medical education by the Carnegie Foundation. Among its recommendations: two-year medical schools should either be phased out or become degree-granting institutions. A concurrent message from President Richard M. Nixon echoed that idea.

Congress then followed through by putting up federal dollars to allow two-year schools to convert to four years. More Congressional encouragement came in the form of one-time capitation grants that would give a medical school up to $50,000 per student if it converted to a four-year degree-granting institution. At the same time, Congress changed the nature of its medical education funding. Research projects were suddenly in disfavor, while those involved in direct education of primary-care doctors got the bulk of the appropriations.

One immediate result was the creation of new medical schools — the Mayo Clinic's program in Rochester, Minnesota, being one of the most notable. But there were others, including several schools established by the Veterans Administration. In further response to the demand for more primary-care physicians, the American Medical Association developed new residency programs in family practice and general internal medicine.

Almost immediately, medical schools nationwide saw a shift in the flow of students into their institutions. Drop-out rates tailed off sharply, as medical schools were now attracting better qualified students in record numbers. In 1972, there were only 13,000 places for 30,000 applicants, and one estimate suggested that 10,000 of those rejected were extremely qualified. Many of those who couldn't get into American medical schools went to foreign schools for two years, hoping to transfer back to the United States for the beginning of their clinical training in the third year. At the same time, more and more graduate students were switching from pure science career paths to medicine.

Suddenly there was unprecedented competition for third-year slots among transfer students. In January 1971, the jarring impact of that phenomenon reached into North Dakota. Letters began arriving at the office of Dr. Wally Nelson, the assistant dean for student affairs at the UND School of Medicine in Grand Forks. Five medical schools that had accepted most of the transfers of UND students in the past told Nelson that they would have difficulty after 1975 in accepting any more students. In subsequent queries, Nelson found that twenty-two of the forty medical schools UND students had transferred to in the past ten years expected problems accepting transfers after 1975.

Up until that moment, UND students had transferred to medical schools all over the United States without much trouble. Much of their success had been based on merit, as evidenced by the number of UND doctors with degrees from Harvard, Yale, Michigan, Minnesota and Washington. Without doubt, some transfers had been made on the basis of political arrangements. At Northwestern, for example, a dean worked out an arrangement with UND's Harwood. By taking that dean's son into the UND medical school, Harwood got Northwestern to agree to take three or four UND transfers every year. Not that UND students couldn't get into a school like Northwestern on merit. In fact, in annual reviews of standardized national test scores of medical students, UND grads regularly placed in the upper quarter. Thanks to Harwood, the school had maintained and even enhanced its solid reputation for its basic science training.

Yet as larger medical schools began feeling the admissions crunch, many of the old arrangements fell by the wayside. At Northwestern, for instance, the retirement of that particular dean dried up several automatic transfer slots for UND students.

"The Northwestern guy was just the tip of the iceberg," recalled Nelson. "Those deals were suddenly out the window. The problem was that, morally, we couldn't continue to accept students into our medical school if we couldn't transfer them."

Nelson was a respected physician and educator, if also a bit of an eccentric. A native of small-town Nebraska, he liked to wear pointy-toed cowboy boots and a ten-gallon hat, and was known for terse and ironic commentary on all aspects of life. These remarks were often laced with humor so dry you didn't know whether to laugh or check for puncture marks. He liked to tell people he was an ornery so and so, but, in truth, he fooled very few. Nelson was a solid doctor with the highest of principles, a man dedicated to student welfare and to medical education. Perhaps most telling, he was a man other

13

doctors trusted and liked. They knew that he knew his stuff, and was blessed with a rare insight.

Nelson was well aware of the ramifications of the transfer problem. For at the time there were but two paths a would-be medical student in North Dakota could follow to become a doctor: apply to a state-run school or to a private school. Across the country nine of every ten students in state-run medical schools were also residents of that state. And about half of the students in private medical schools lived in the same state as the college they attended.

Those numbers pointed up the tremendous difficulty that a North Dakota student faced in being accepted into a medical school outside the state. From 1964 to 1971, of the 359 North Dakota students who entered medical school, 312 attended UND, and only forty-seven — or six a year — were accepted by medical schools outside the state.

Nelson was the first at UND to appreciate the gravity of the situation. Two-year-medical schools were about to go the way of the buffalo. It meant, perhaps, shutting down UND's medical school. That would mean even fewer doctors in the state's already doctor-starved small communities.

In a letter to the dean of the medical school at Iowa, Nelson acknowledged the warning. "The handwriting," he said, "is on the wall."

Mustang out of Langdon

2

Quite apart from the sweeping changes that jolted the stability of the medical school at UND in 1970, another social upheaval had simultaneously brought disruption to the campus. That tempest was the Vietnam War — or more precisely, the mounting national protest against the war. In a very short space of time, and with more than a little irony, these two completely distinct forces came together in a way that no one would have thought remotely plausible.

For the sudden crisis over the medical school presented itself at the very moment that a most unlikely leader was emerging at the university, almost through the back door. And as it happened, the cold nerve and delicate wit required to overcome the complex political hurdles standing in the way of a rebirth at the medical school, were precisely the qualities Tom Clifford displayed in dealing with war protestors. They were qualities Clifford had been honing to perfection his entire life, and they brought him to the fore now.

The full story of the one cannot be told or appreciated without also hearing the story of the other.

Here is what happened: In May 1970, National Guard troops at Kent State University in Ohio shot and killed four students who were part of a larger protest demonstration against the war. Campuses nationwide had been seething with anti-war protest for more than two years. The invasion of Cambodia and the Kent State tragedy unleashed even more passionate and potentially destructive demonstrations and rallies at colleges almost everywhere. In Grand Forks, heavily attended protest rallies at the Memorial Student Union had already pilloried the university's once-respected president, George Starcher. An Army Reserve Officer Training Corps program and the campus Armory that housed it, had became lightning rods for protesters looking for a way to vent their anger and fear.

On the day after the Kent State shootings, 700 students gathered on the Grand Forks campus and marched on the Armory. Ugly rumors ran ahead of them: they intended to burn the building down. President Starcher was out of town that day, and so Tom Clifford, his vice-president of finance, decided to walk across campus to see what he could do.

Clifford at fifty was a large, athletic man with one of those ruddy Celtic faces and a set of Irish blue eyes that were usually quick to smile. But on this day he kept the smile hidden, although as he walked toward the crowd in his double breasted suit, he chortled to himself that he must look to the students like a mafia thug. In truth he brought an unusual set of values to the Armory that afternoon, values strangely balanced across the spectrum of both peace and war.

Twenty-eight years earlier, in January 1942, the 21-year-old Tom Clifford had enlisted as a private in the U.S. Marine Corps. He was recruited by Evan Lips, a former teammate on the UND football team. Lips, who would one day serve three terms as mayor of Bismarck and thirty-eight years in the State Senate, had joined the Marines a year earlier following his own graduation. He'd been sent back to campus after Pearl Harbor to sign up others.

Clifford might have gone to war, as many of his classmates did, as an Army second lieutenant. But ever since his arrival at Grand Forks from tiny Langdon, North Dakota, he had stubbornly refused to participate in the ROTC program. He played football hard, but talked of being a pacifist and was nearly expelled for his refusal to take ROTC classes. He weathered it all because trouble had been his middle name for some time.

Back in Langdon, Clifford's father, Thomas, had been a successful lawyer and banker. He owned a large house on the edge of town and a ranch a little bit farther west. It was there that young Tommy spent his summers, dreaming of a life raising Hereford steers. He'd been a sickly boy, born with smallpox and hobbled by severe asthma at the age of six. The local doctor, a man named McQueen, told his mother to cut off a pair of overalls and let Tommy spend the summer without a shirt out on the ranch. It worked. The asthma disappeared forever.

Meanwhile, the elder Clifford was a complicated man, as well-versed in poetry as in law. He held a degree from Trinity College in Dublin and Tommy remembers him "as a kind man but somewhat impractical." Tommy's father and grandfather also were Irish veterans of the British Army. The grandfather fought with the Irish Guards in the Sudan against the Mahdi and the Fuzzy Wuzzys of Kipling fame. His father fought in the Boer War with the Coldstream Guards. The elder Clifford insisted that his son Tommy read volumes of military history, which he did. Stories about war were common and Tommy sometimes got carried away. One day, playing at soldier, he shot a neighbor's cat from a bedroom window. Eventually, though, he got fed up with war stories and developed an aversion to all things military. Whether or not that was a rebellion against his father, Clifford admits today the two never got along that well. "It was our nature," he says simply. "We had our conflicts."

Following his career in the Coldstream Guards, Clifford's father had come to America and done some amateur boxing. He then hired

on with the Great Northern Railroad as a telegrapher and was post-
ed to North Dakota. There he married and divorced before he met
Elizabeth, soon to be Clifford's mother.

They settled in Langdon, a quiet wheat town of about 2,000,
built by French, Irish, Scottish and German immigrants on rolling
terrain at the edge of the Red River Valley. East of it, along the Pem-
bina River there was always plenty of elk, deer and wild turkey to
hunt. The town had a wide Main Street, lots of trees in the residen-
tial sector and homes that were well kept. There was also a smatter-
ing of the Ku Klux Klan in the area, and religious bigotry ran high.
The great division lay between the Catholics and the Protestants.

The priests at St. Alphonsus, the Roman Catholic school where
Tommy attended through the eighth grade, wouldn't allow him or
others to join the Boy Scouts — because it was the Presbyterians
who ran that franchise. Tommy and his friends looked on the Scouts
as the enemy. The Scouts met every Sunday night at church and he
recalls it well. "We'd stand outside the church — the Irish and Ger-
mans and French guys, and we'd catch those Scouts coming out and
we'd beat the hell out of them. I swear I made one guy a miler."

That boy was named Gardner. Tommy Clifford chased him
home every Sunday night. Once Gardner's mother came out of the
house and broke a broom over Tommy's head. "It was that kind of a
thing," Clifford recalls today. "It seems kind of barbaric now, but it
was real then."

Tommy did have a few saving graces. The first was a joy for reading. In later years he would tell people that the best teacher he ever
had was Sister Mary Helen Austin in the first grade at St. Alphonus.
She taught him to read.

"But," people would ask, "wasn't that her job? What makes that
so great?"

"Because," Clifford smiles, "she taught me to like it."

Young Tommy was also a bit fearless. He used to play handball
with the tough priests at St. Alphonsus, who always seemed stern

and held him to a strict standard of discipline. But he adapted to the tough stuff until it rolled off his back like rain. He become such a hard case, in fact, that after he completed the eighth grade the weary priests asked him not to re-enroll at St. Alphonsus for high school.

"It wasn't their fault," he remembers today. "My dad had died and I was kind of rebellious. I was a cantankerous guy. I had a lot of energy."

Thomas Clifford was killed in an automobile accident when Tommy was thirteen. Because his father had already suffered heavy losses in the Great Depression, Clifford's family was left with substantial land but not much money. Suddenly they had to scrape along and do without. In the meantime, Tommy had no choice but to attend public school with the very Protestant boys he'd beaten up every week. Even so, he wouldn't let the fear of reprisals keep him from going out for football — although during the first week of practice he sat warily on the end of the bench. Within two weeks the situation had been diffused, thanks to an understanding coach named Kilpatrick who molded Tommy and his old enemies into a team. With a legitimate outlet now for his energy, he pounded his way to a satisfying high school football career.

Perhaps the greatest saving grace in his life was his mother, Elizabeth, whom he found more caring and more influential in his life than his father. When it came time to go to college, Tommy remembers he would just as soon have stayed in Langdon and raised Herefords. "But my mother came to the ranch, packed up my stuff and took me down to Grand Forks to school. I was always very grateful to her. Because when I got here I loved it. I didn't want to go home."

It wasn't without fear that Clifford approached the jittery crowd of protesters that spring day in 1970.

"I'll never forget that smell," he says. "There was an animal-like smell among them. They were all of them all excited — and sweating; there was that smell of perspiration. Not of a skunk, exactly, but you exude it with fear. I walked through there and I didn't know if they might shoot me. My armpits were wet."

At the Armory he met with the chief of police and an Army colonel. Those two men were wringing their hands with worry, almost begging Clifford for ideas on what to do. Meanwhile, outside the Armory, students had started beating large drums. Someone threw a rock and broke a window. The ROTC colonel started shaking in his boots.

"I looked out a window," recalls Clifford, "and could see these guys and I knew they were going to burn the Armory down. It would have been such a bad thing for the university."

Clifford turned to the two men.

"Let's get the hell out there," he said. "We've got to face them."

But, the colonel whined, "They'll destroy this place."

Disgusted, Clifford led them outside and the three men stood facing the forward edge of the crowd. He looked at the colonel and saw that his leg was shaking. He leaned over and growled, "Cut the goddam shaking."

The colonel stared at Clifford.

"Tell 'em something," said Clifford. "Anything."

But the man couldn't find his voice. So Clifford faced the crowd. He had two thoughts. He might feel fear but he was damned if he'd let anyone see his leg shaking. He also knew just what he wanted to do.

He wanted to fight in the Pacific.

With war almost certainly coming, Tom Clifford had a difficult choice to make in late 1941 about his pacifism. In spite of, or perhaps because of, his forced reading of military history as a boy, he saw no reason for war. He remembers himself as an impressionable, naive boy, profoundly influenced by North Dakota's senior United States senator, Gerald P. Nye. The well known Nye Commission had already sparked controversy by claiming that America entered

World War I strictly to make weapons manufacturers wealthy. On the eve of World War II, Nye was a leading isolationist and claimed among his followers the national hero Col. Charles A. Lindbergh.

"It wasn't very smart for me to be like that," Clifford recalls today. "I wasn't very perceptive. Hitler was shaking up western Europe."

Yet one of his concerns had to do with his mother's ethnic origins. She was a native of Austria and Tom had several cousins in Germany. The prospect of fighting against those cousins did not sit well with him.

Then the Japanese attacked Pearl Harbor and everything became much clearer.

"That really ticked me off when the Japanese attacked us," he says. "Quite honestly, I thought I'd rather fight in the jungle than in the snow. Being from North Dakota, if I'm shooting guns I want to be where it's warm."

So he agreed with his former teammate Evan Lips to join up. Clifford had to go through basic Marine boot camp as a private, after which he was eligible to attend the even tougher Marine officer's course.

Just after he was commissioned a second lieutenant, he married his college sweetheart, Florence. Typically, he got in trouble for it. For Florence was a German Baptist, and Clifford an Irish Catholic. Parents on both sides were against the marriage. As the families argued, Clifford showed the stirrings of his lifelong impatience with delays. "I said I've only got so much time. Let's elope."

So they did, finding a Methodist minister in Montana to perform the quick ceremony. He and Florence went to San Clemente, California, where Clifford had one last round of training before shipping out. Wracked by guilt for marrying outside the Catholic Church, he wrote a letter to the cardinal who acted as liaison between the church and the military. The result: just before he shipped out, Tom and Florence were married again, this time in the Church of Angels in Oceanside.

With only the barest taste of married life, Clifford suddenly had to settle into an even odder marriage: life as a Marine. "But the Marine Corps did a lot for me," he says. "I liked the discipline, I liked the training. It was rigorous, but I knew we had to do it. It really squared me away."

"Squared away" to a Marine, however, has nothing to do with staying out of trouble. If anything, it's the opposite, especially in places like Guadalcanal, Iwo Jima and Saipan. It was on those islands that young Tom Clifford became the warrior he never expected to be, for he'd taken to his new surroundings as if he'd been born to it. From a private in basic training to a commissioned second lieutenant, the maverick from Langdon had risen to become a mustang Marine officer.

He saw brutal action on the tiny island of Iwo Jima, where the Marines lost almost 7,000 killed and 20,000 wounded. Clifford had been trained as a tank commander, and his tanks were involved in an attack on one of the two Japanese airfields on Iwo, up on the Motoyama Plateau. Not only did the Marines want to seize the airfields for use by their own planes, they needed to keep the Japanese from using the plateau as a base for firing onto the beachhead below. As the result of the bitter fighting for those airfields, the Japanese were pushed off the plateau and toward the northern end of island. When the smoke cleared, Clifford was awarded a Silver Star for heroism.

When he tells the story, though, he says it this way. "We got the Silver Star after we knocked off a counter attack ... "

We?

"I've always felt that," he says. "I was the commander, but there were other guys in that tank with me. They didn't get anything. But they were right there. They had no choice. Later, after action on Saipan, I got the Bronze Star and afterwards we all went down to the bar and I had my crew with me and we all celebrated. Those guys were terrific."

The strain of combat, however, didn't seem to affect Clifford's sense of humor. "We were in a tank once," he says, smiling, "and a shell blew up underneath me." In fact, he was wounded in that explosion. But he doesn't mention that at all. Instead he follows up with a grin and adds, as only Clifford could, "I've got a funny story about that."

It seems that the armor plating on the light tanks used by Marines was at its thinnest on the tank's underside. The one thing tank crews feared more than being killed was being emasculated by such an explosion. On Saipan, between operations, the adjutant of the regiment stopped by Clifford's outfit one afternoon and was puzzled to see him working his crews so hard. Most units used the rare downtime between firefights for rest. But beneath a blazing sun, Clifford's men were working feverishly with welding torches, and weren't grousing about it. The adjutant couldn't believe it.

"Lieutenant," he said, "How do you get these guys working like this?"

"Oh," shrugged Clifford, "they're pretty good about this maintenance."

Clifford received a commendation for such leadership, an award that today he laughs off. "What we were doing was welding steel plates in there so we wouldn't get our balls shot off."

He is quick to say that he was never the classic officer. But he was a fast study. Survival in combat, he learned — he was awarded three purple hearts for various wounds — required just the right balance of risk taking and patience.

"I didn't rush foolishly into things," he recalls. "When I got an order I'd contemplate that."

A good example is what happened during the battles on Saipan. It was one of the islands in the Marianas that the Navy needed so it could launch air strikes against mainland Japan. Clifford's tank company was spread out facing a sheer cliffside. The Japanese were dug in at the top and the approaches to the cliff were well covered by their artillery.

Clifford's radio sputtered. A colonel stationed in a cave far behind the lines ordered him to assault the cliff with his tanks.

"I looked at that and I said to myself, 'If we go up there we're gonna lose tanks and people.' It was impossible. It was not pretty smart. I thought about that. I said, 'Gee this'll probably get a bunch of people killed, including myself. And if I don't do it, it's insubordination. I don't want to get a court martial. And I don't want to appear that I'm not ready to fight.'"

Clifford, who earlier had been promoted to captain, quickly switched channels on the radio and got hold of his tank commanders. He told them they'd been ordered to attack, but he had a better idea. He told them to gun their engines, to make a lot of smoke and shoot off all their ammunition.

"We've got to make a big show of this," he said. "When I give a command, fire everything you've got. Roar your motors, but don't move."

That's what they did. They fired thousands of rounds of ammunition against the cliff that no tank commander, not even Patton, would have considering assaulting.

"We roared the damn engines. Dust was blowing. We had a firestorm. Smoke and flashes. The goddang Japanese thought we were crazy. I kept that up for about twenty minutes."

The radio crackled again. It was the colonel.

"Well done, Captain," he said crisply. "That's the way to do it."

"I don't think we can go any further, sir," said Clifford.

"Very well," came the reply. "You've done a marvelous job."

The situation was resolved shortly afterward when the big guns of naval battleships sitting off the coast opened up on the cliff and a group of infantry was sent in to mop up.

"I think that's where I could have killed a lot of people and not accomplished anything. Or I could have gotten court-martialed," he says today. "Hell, that situation didn't call for tank warfare. You have to stop and look at it for a minute. Now, some guys killed a lot of guys that way. I conserved my men pretty good. I brought my guys back. It was one thing I was pretty proud of. When our guys got wounded and sent to the rear, those guys would hitch rides across ocean to come back to the outfit. It made me feel real good. They knew you were taking care of them. It's not as if we didn't have heavy, heavy casualties in the outfit. But I learned that day you don't kill yourself over some damn fool."

Clifford had been eyeing a large man standing in the front row of the mob of protesters, somebody he didn't recognize as a UND student.

"Hey," he said, stepping up to him. "What's on your mind?"

The man was taken aback.

"I don't recall seeing you here before," pushed Clifford. "Did you just come into town?"

"Uh, well."

"Look," said Clifford, "tell me what you want to do, will ya? Just tell me."

When he got no answer, he turned the question to others nearby.

"Or any of you. Explain it to me why you're here."

But nobody in the crowd would meet his eyes.

"Aw the hell with it," said the big man in the front row finally. "Let's go."

With that the crowd began to disband.

Clifford, though, didn't relax. He confronted several female students trying to tear down the American flag as they left. He grabbed the first one by the arm.

"What are you doing here?" Clifford suddenly realized he knew the girl's father. "I'm sure your dad would be real proud of you. Now you get yourself over to that Gamma Phi house and clean up. I don't want to see you around here again. Okay?"

She and the others retreated in haste as Clifford secured the flag. Watching them go, he didn't know whether to feel good or bad.

"I didn't like the war any better than they did," he recalls. "I felt we'd made some huge mistakes in the war. But that wasn't the way. Those guys over there deserve your support. So I faced them down."

Afterwards, some remarked that it was a good thing Starcher hadn't been in town that day. He would never have done what Clifford did. Clifford knew it and so did Starcher. The man had been president at UND since 1955, a mathematician, an academician, a capable organization man who'd done much to improve the university curriculum. He'd increased the faculty, built up the library and strengthened the school academically. Early on he'd made a deal with Clifford. I'll handle the academics, you handle the street side of things. The two men got on well, the warrior and the academic, each with deep respect for the other.

"When the protests started, I watched with some chagrin the way the faculty and the students turned on him," says Clifford today. "He got a bum rap in many ways. His ideas were just tremendous. What a good guy. But they'd be chanting in front of his house and knocking on his door. I told him to ignore that, but he couldn't. I still remember they had a meeting they invited him to at which they crucified him. I remember I walked with him over to the Student Union where they were having this big rally. No one else in the faculty would walk with him. It hurt his feelings really bad."

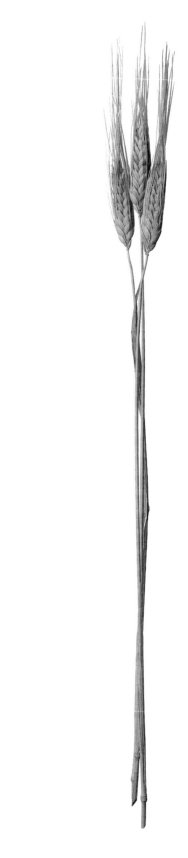

Outsmarting the Mamelukes

3

Not long after the incident at the Armory, Starcher announced his retirement as president of UND. Immediately a search committee of faculty members came together to look for a replacement. Perhaps it was Clifford's coolness in facing down the mob that moved the committee to invite him to apply for the job. But the very same traits unnerved some among the faculty. In a sense, Clifford was the antithesis of what they wanted. He was a warrior, not an academic. Thus, when they submitted their final list of three names to the state's Board of Higher Education, the body that would do the actual hiring, the name Tom Clifford wasn't on it.

"I used to describe a professor," says Clifford today, "as a guy who thought otherwise. An academic is a special person in our society. They're thoughtful and for the most part aren't grasping. They are people who take pride in what they know. They have a very high priority in learning. And a degree means a lot to them. I always thought a degree was nice but not the only thing. So I guess in that sense I differ. I have a lot of good friends in academics. I treated them with respect but I didn't always think they were right. They would do foolish things in life that really didn't enhance their prestige or their welfare. But they didn't understand it. They had a different measure. If they got an article published somewhere, even if it was not a very good one, it was a big contribution to civilization. They didn't realize how ephemeral it was. I shouldn't be too hard on them, but in a lot of ways they just don't get it. And besides, I always worked both sides of the street."

Clifford began walking that street almost as soon as he returned from the war. But not before he nearly left North Dakota to make his fortune elsewhere. He'd been accepted to the University of Michigan's law school and had it in mind to become a lawyer and make a lot of money — and fast. Because of his multiple war wounds and the tropical diseases like dengue fever that had wracked his body in the Pacific, he'd gotten it into his head that he didn't have long to live.

But Michigan couldn't admit him until February of 1946. That left him with four months of just hanging around in Grand Forks. In the meantime, R.D. Koppenhaver, one of his professors and the man who chaired the accounting department, asked him to fill in for a teacher who had become ill. Clifford, who'd earned his degree in accounting, agreed and found teaching to his liking. At the end of the semester, the same professor persuaded him to go to law school in Grand Forks and work simultaneously as a teacher. That was the end of Michigan.

Meanwhile, the president of UND at the time, John West, had taken a liking to Clifford and made him an offer he couldn't refuse. The campus was flooded with returning veterans, and West wanted a dean of men who knew how to handle them and shape them into students. Clifford agreed and ruled with the discipline of a Marine. So much so that West complained to him, "Tommy, you've thrown more people out of school in the last four or five months than we have in the past twenty years."

Clifford agreed to back off. But that very night two students come back to campus at 3 A.M., beered up and singing at the top of their lungs. Their residence hall was right next to the president's house. West suffered from bronchitis and had trouble sleeping. The next morning, as Clifford remembers it, West called him up and barked, "Get those guys who were singing and kick 'em out."

"Well, wait a minute, chief," said Clifford. "You told me to ease off."

"Never mind!"

So Clifford called in the two offending students. Likely he couldn't help seeing himself in them and remembering some of the wild stunts he'd pulled while in the Marines. Once, when his outfit had come back from the fighting to Hawaii, they were told they couldn't go on liberty without military insignia on their uniforms. But they'd lost their insignia during heavy combat. Clifford and a friend fixed that by sneaking into the coat room at the officers' club and pinching insignia off uniform jackets. They distributed them to their comrades, who were then able to get a pass and let off some steam. Even more delightful was watching the military police searching high and low for the missing pins. That had been fun.

The students before him were Bohemian kids from Pisek, North Dakota. Clifford sighed and told them he had to do something about them. Once again, though, he didn't storm the cliff.

"They were good kids, you know? They got drunk. They weren't malicious or anything. And they were smart. And so why waste that?"

He told them they could stay in school on the condition they move out of their residence hall so the president would see something had been done. Second, they had to join Kappa Sigma, which had been Clifford's fraternity and was looking for members. They agreed and they became his lifelong friends.

The young dean of men made a lot of deals like that with students. It was part of working the other side of the street. He even borrowed an idea from his Marine Corps days. During the war he used to win substantial amounts of money playing blackjack poker with hapless sailors. He'd dole it out, ten or twenty bucks at a time, to the men in his tank platoon. Government paychecks were always months behind during the war.

"Our guys didn't have any money and that meant a lot to them," he says. "They'd be able to go out on liberty. I'd tell 'em you can pay me back whenever you want. It wasn't a lot of money. They hadn't had milkshakes — hell, most of 'em probably spent it on booze. But that's just little ways how you do things. I just felt that's the way to do it. I wasn't that close to them. I wasn't going out drinking with my guys. That's no way to do it, because we all have feet of clay and you get out there and they see that you really don't know a hell of a lot."

He tried the same thing at Grand Forks, advancing hard-up students a few bucks here and there. Many of them never forgot the kindness, and almost all of them repaid the loans. Years later, in fact, when he was president, Clifford was pressing the flesh at a fundraiser. A man and his wife came up to him. Clifford vaguely remembered the man as an engineering student in the class he taught on business law. He reminded Clifford of the time he was strapped for cash and didn't have enough food for his family. Clifford had given him $20 so he could buy some oatmeal and groceries until his check came in. He'd paid back the loan, he told Clifford that night, and had come to the fundraiser to make an $8,000 donation in memory of that kindness.

"That touched my heart," says Clifford now. "You know, I only had one guy stiff me. And that guy was never successful. I know, because I followed him. I'm Irish. The only thing an Irishman with Alzheimer's never forgets is a grudge."

After law school in 1948, Clifford had several job offers and was all set to hang out his shingle. But John West called him in again. He told him he should stay in education. He offered to make him dean of the business school.

But Clifford was hesitant. "God, John," he said. "I want to make money."

West, though, knew he had him.

"You know what you do here, Tommy? You help people. That'll be there for a long time. If you become a lawyer, I know you'll be successful, but after you close a case and they've paid you and you shut the brief, then that's it."

That made the twenty-seven-year-old think.

"So I went home and I said to my wife, what do you think? She said, 'Well, I love the campus, the music and fine arts.' She was a concert pianist. She said, 'We can get by. We don't need a lot of money.'"

Clifford went back the next day and told West he was concerned that he didn't have the fancy degree he'd need to be working alongside pure academics. He asked for and was granted a year's leave of absence to go to Stanford for an MBA. While there he was awarded a Sloan Fellowship and even entered a doctoral program.

He came back to UND before that degree was completed. But the transformation of Clifford the warrior to Clifford the academic was already under way, orchestrated by John West. The two became very close. Clifford called him chief and West called him Tommy.

Clifford found West to be thoughtful but also full of useful tricks. For instance, West, a refined academic, always presented himself to the State Legislature in Bismarck as something of a hick. He wore socks that didn't match and he'd adopt soft country expressions he never used in Grand Forks. He'd talk to them about something being "between the hay and the straw."

Of course, the legislators loved him.

"He was a hell of a guy," says Clifford. "I learned a lot from him. He was bright and he knew who he had to deal with. You might think that hick stuff was phony, but he did it masterfully."

West was nearly seventy and Clifford twenty-eight. Though he had a personal driver, whenever West went to Bismarck, it was Tommy who drove for him.

"He was tighter than hell," recalls Clifford. "He didn't have any money. He was only getting about $4,000 a year as president. He'd been superintendent of schools in Grand Forks. A lot of faculty members around the state — the high-degreed guys — held him in contempt. They looked down upon him. Hell, he was smarter than any of them."

To illustrate his chief's wily ways of dealing with know-it-all faculty members, Clifford recalls one morning that a self-aggrandizing history professor came to see West about a problem with one of his employees. "God, he was a pompous guy," remembers Clifford, who was in the office that day. "West said, 'You want me to write him a letter?' This professor said yes. So John dictated the damndest letter on an old Dictaphone. The professor just thought it was great. When he was done, John said, 'How was that, Doctor?' Well, he thought it was just wonderful. Then I happened to look over at the Dictaphone and there was no belt on it. He'd never recorded the damn thing."

Then, of course, there was the seminal incident of the swimming pool.

The university had built a new physical education building but lacked the state funding for a pool. West went ahead and dug the hole anyway. Clifford arranged with the accounting department to transfer the money to pay for it.

In Bismarck, when the legislature heard about it, they raised hell. They sent for West, who drove down with Tommy. There he was upbraided by angry legislators for his wanton act.

"They said to him, 'You put this pool in?'

"He said, 'We had permission; we just didn't have the money.'"

Afterwards, as they drove back to Grand Forks, they heard a radio news report about what a terrible whipping West had been given by the legislators for putting in the pool. The whole time, West sat back in his seat with his hat on, smoking a cigar. He liked to smoke them with the cellophane still attached. Clifford looked over at him and said, "What do you think of that, chief?"

West took a puff from his cigar.

"Well, Tommy," he said, "we're swimming in it aren't we?'

It was not only the perfect squelch, it was a remark that formed part of the bedrock of Clifford's values as a leader. He learned that it was easier to ask for forgiveness than permission. Years later, as president, Clifford wanted to build a road on the south end of the campus along the railroad tracks. This time he had the money but he didn't have the permission from the Board of Higher Education. He built the road anyway. When he saw the road, the university's building and grounds supervisor was amazed.

"Tom," he said, "you got to get permission from the board to put that in." Clifford's reply was predictable. "Well, Gordon," he said, "we're driving on it, aren't we?"

One of the great imponderables about North Dakota — a state that relies on itself for so much; a place where independence and grit are prized and outsiders viewed with some suspicion — is how difficult it is to become a dean or the president of the University of North Dakota if you're from North Dakota.

It seems that search committees have forever looked afar, rather than near for the next person to lead them. There are several theories to explain this. One cynical argument suggests that the word undeserving begins with the letters UND. Another reminds that the prophet is never appreciated in his own land, and of course there's always the grass-is-greener-anywhere-else theory.

To this, Dr. Bob Eelkema adds his Mameluke theory.

"In ancient Egypt they figured that the citizens couldn't run their own business so they hired Turkish people to come in. They were the Mamelukes. They were the paid leaders of Egypt because they figured they were too dumb to lead themselves."

Thus it was, says Eelkema that in 1971 the faculty committee charged with finding a replacement for George Starcher submitted a list of non-North Dakota presidential candidates to the state Board of Higher Education.

But along with the hoary Mameluke theory, there is another perhaps more abiding rule of thumb that overshadowed all others in

1971. Known to the uninitiated as "Semper Fidelis," or to those who have actually been to the Halls of Montezuma as "Semper Fi," this rule ordains that Marines take care of Marines.

When last we saw Evan Lips, he was recruiting Tom Clifford into the Marine Corps in January 1942. Lips himself saw considerable combat in the South Pacific as a Marine and to this day will note rather dryly that Tom Clifford never properly thanked him for persuading him to follow the eagle, globe and anchor.

To that, Clifford offers the following belated appreciation: "When I was getting shelled in foxholes, I interspersed my prayers with a 'Goddam you, Evan Lips!' I thought about him a lot when I was out there getting the hell blown out of me."

Boys will be boys and Marines will be Marines. Lips went on to become a prominent and influential state senator from Bismarck. In 1971 he looked with great displeasure at the list of Mamelukes submitted to the Board of Higher Education. Lips and another Marine, Earl Strinden, who was a powerful state representative from Grand Forks, began an intense, behind-the-scenes campaign on Clifford's behalf. Legislators began calling the members of the state board to inquire about a certain name left off a certain list.

It wasn't just Clifford's Marine status that swayed votes, however. As UND's vice-president of finance, Clifford had gone before dozens of legislative committees in the past and he knew almost everybody by first name. He was one of those people nobody but an academic could dislike.

"He could talk to any committee without any notes at all about any aspect of the university," says Lips. "The medical school, engineering, the art school. He knew the ins and outs of the university like nobody else. He was very intelligent and a man who never said no to anything."

Somebody once asked Clifford if he wasn't afraid to go before the legislature. "Listen, baby," he said, "if you were in the third wave at Iwo Jima, you're not afraid of any guy, and I don't really give a damn." To Bob Eelkema, he confided that if things didn't work out he'd simply go back to Langdon and raise Herefords.

But in a twinkling, a fourth name was added to the list of presidential candidates. And when the state board voted, Clifford was their unanimous choice. Not one to show he had been anxious, Clifford demurred for twenty-four hours to consider the offer. On the handball court that afternoon, he and Eelkema shared a hearty laugh at such nerve. The next day he agreed to become the eighth president in the school's history.

No sooner had he taken office than Clifford went head to head with some of the academics who had openly campaigned against him. There were two men in particular, one a vice-president with whom he had worked in the business school.

"We'd been friends, but he didn't think I was an academic," he recalls. "And that's fine. So I called him in on a Friday. I said now I know you did everything in the world to keep me from being president. But that's past. I said I don't know how you feel about it, but I want you to go home over the weekend and I want you to write down how you can work with me. And I'm going to write down how I can work with you. And we're going to have a little list on Monday morning and we'll see where we stand. Well, on Monday morning he came in and we squared it all off. And he stayed and he was the best guy I ever had. He didn't think I was the guy for it and I understood that. But he worked fanatically for me."

With a second opponent, a dean, things didn't go as smoothly.

"He was mean to people," says Clifford. "I called him in and I said I know you didn't want me to be president but I am. You know what we're going to do? We're going to do things my way. I didn't give him an option. I said now these are some of the things that you're going to have to correct. I said I know for a fact that you don't have any guts. Because I watch how you treat people and you treat them with the mark of cowardice. And I really don't like that. But I do respect your knowledge. Now if you can handle that and start cleaning up your act then we can get together. But I said the minute you start slipping back, you're history. I said I'll find a way to get rid of you. You're an administrative appointment, you can stay as a professor, but I'll bury you in the chemistry department. He said fine. He was always afraid of me, he never liked me, but we got along."

Clifford had one more adversary to face that first day in office.

"I drank too much," he says. "I didn't drink until I was in the Marine Corps, and even then I didn't drink every day. But when I went out I always had a good time. As president you go to about eighteen cocktail parties a month, and I had to make a decision whether I was going to be a drunk or whether I was going to do the job. So I quit, cold turkey, on New Year's Day. I got up with a hangover and I said screw this. I said North Dakota people don't like presidents who get drunk and bite women on the ankles. It was one of those terrible curses, and it was a tough decision. But I never missed it. I was pretty damn lucky."

"Who the Hell Is Eelkema?"

4

In Grand Forks, Dr. Wally Nelson was just beginning to spread the news of the looming transfer crisis among a handful of medical school colleagues. They included Dean Harwood, of course, the man who had run the school for eighteen years. To some, though, Harwood seemed almost uninterested in the problem.

"He just seemed desperately old," recalls Bill Harlan, the doctor from Duke who would later serve as a consultant. "He wasn't vigorous. He seemed mired sort of in the 1890s."

In fact, Harwood was ill, showing initial signs of the cancer that would eventually kill him. He was known by many as "Apple Cider and Honey," because he liked to talk of Vermont, his home state. Indeed, one of the reasons Harwood had been brought to North Dakota was the University of Vermont's success in converting its two-year medical school to a full four-year program. Yet almost from the day Harwood arrived in Grand Forks, he had refused to believe that North Dakota could do likewise — citing the state's small population and what he considered insufficient clinical resources.

Even so, Harwood had done a great deal for the two-year program, most notably expanding the basic science departments from three to six faculty members each. A scholarly, private, frugal man who sang in the First Presbyterian choir, he was well liked on campus, especially by students. He was an old-school dean who made a point of knowing as much about his students as possible. His nurturing style provided a personal touch in their education that many found regrettably absent when they transferred to larger, impersonal schools for their third and fourth years of training.

"Ted was a fine man," says John Vennes, Ph.D., the well-thought-of microbiologist who chaired the medical school's curriculum committee at the time.

Vennes was one of the handful who worried over Nelson's news. He'd grown up in the Depression in the tiny western North Dakota town of Zall. Though it was not far from Williston, the nearest almost-big city, times were so hard that few residents were able to get out of Zall.

Ultimately it was the Navy that fostered Vennes's interest in science. As a corpsman during World War II, he served in naval hospitals and became interested through labs and x-rays in the biological sciences. When, after the war, he earned his undergraduate and master's degrees in biology at UND he was asked to stay on and teach.

Once Harwood arrived in 1953, the two men got to know each other. Learning that Vennes wanted to get a Ph.D., Harwood arranged financial support that allowed Vennes to go to the University of Michigan and earn his doctoral degree. All the time in Michigan, Vennes never thought of anything else but returning to Grand Forks, where he became a mainstay of the faculty.

Another in Nelson's coterie was the man everyone called Moses.

"He was a tall stately guy, very astute, very articulate," recalls Clifford. "And physically impressive. Almost gruff looking. He looked liked Moses. It looked like he was handing down the tablets of rock all the time."

His name was Willard Wright. Born in Manitoba in 1899, he'd gone to medical school in Winnipeg and in Edinburgh, Scotland, where he passed the examination to become a fellow of the Royal College of Surgeons. After serving in the Canadian Army during World War I, the young and restless Dr. Wright wandered down into North Dakota, eventually settling in Williston by 1930. He and John Vennes had more in common than the medical school, for it had been Wright who delivered the future Dr. Vennes in Zall.

"He had a great reputation in North Dakota medicine," says Clifford. "They thought the world of him in Williston, as did the medical profession at large. He was the real McCoy."

In fact he'd been president of the North Dakota Medical Association and had risen to the number two slot in the American Medical Association. By 1971, Wright, retired from his Williston practice, had been named director of a federal Regional Medical Program set up to deal with problems of heart, cancer and stroke. It was a job that brought him frequently to Grand Forks to work closely on a project with another of Nelson's group, Dr. Bob Eelkema.

"I always felt Willard was my mentor," says Eelkema. "Not just because he was much older than I, but also because I learned a great deal from him. He taught me how to set up a receptive framework for a project and showed me how not to be discouraged. He was tall, bald, commanding. He looked to me more like Genghis Khan than Moses. He was actually easy going, easy to like. He didn't have an I-know-it-all personality — meaning he wasn't a typical surgeon. But underneath that genial exterior, he was politically savvy and he knew how to get things done."

Eelkema was in many respects the perfect student for Willard Wright. He didn't fit the mold of a medical school professor. He'd begun his career as a veterinarian but says he left it for human medicine because he simply got tired of castrating bulls. Friends would agree that Eelkema has always had a knack for being in the right place at the right time. Also, like Rafael Sabatini's *Scaramouche*, he seems to have been "born with a gift of laughter and a sense that the world was mad." When it came to the buttoned down minds of bureaucracy and their endless lists of do's and don'ts — mostly don'ts — Eelkema seemed fearless. Perhaps it had something to do with his colorblindness. Just as he often wore maroon shirts with clashing burgundy pants, he would sometimes confuse red with green and barge through academic stoplights trailing a hearty Dutch laugh.

Bobby Eelkema was the son of a Dutch educator-turned-farmer, and a Norwegian mother, both raised in Iowa. It was prowess at baseball that got Herman Henry Eelkema into college. There he met and eloped with Ruth Naomi Young in 1916 — only to have her parents drag them into a church a year later and have them married a second time just to be sure.

The senior Eelkema — known to many as H.H., or Prof — was a driven man. He became superintendent of schools in Drayton, North Dakota, in 1916, where he earned $450 a year. But by pitching for the town's team in the summer, he earned an extra $75 a game. It was around Drayton, where land was still being homesteaded, that Herman Eelkema began buying up acreage for farming. But that career had to wait, as his career as an educator took him to South Dakota, Minnesota, Illinois, Iowa, Virginia and back again to Minnesota. Along the way, Herman Eelkema earned a Ph.D. and a law degree in the same year. After Robert was born in Mankato in 1930, the family settled in Duluth, where H.H. was superintendent for many years.

By the end of World War II, he tired of education and moved the family back to Drayton to begin a life of farming. It was there while sewing potato sacks that the sixteen-year-old Robert realized that if he wanted to get anywhere in life he'd need to dig into education. He went to the University of Minnesota-Duluth, where he played football, broke his nose and cracked his teeth. He eventually got into veterinary school not because of his great passion for animals, but because of his disarming candor. He told the acceptance committee he needed some sort of livelihood if he was going to get a loan to start a farm. They were bowled over by his lack of pretense.

Eelkema began his veterinary practice in 1956 in Valley City, North Dakota, but soon realized his heart wasn't in it. He toyed with applying for medical school but put it off until the day a farmer in Castleton hired him to castrate 200 head of Angus bulls. The regular vet had a broken leg and had asked Eelkema to fill in.

"I figured they would be young calves," he says. "But they were all eighteen months old with huge testicles. I cut out 400 of 'em. It was a very warm day and I had to jump from one animal to the next to avoid those kicks. I thought, 'Geez, if I get out of this alive I'll put my application in to medical school.'"

From 1957 to 1959 he studied medicine at UND in Grand Forks, where he also met a handball player named Tom Clifford. Eelkema finished his medical degree at the University of Washington in Seattle and decided to pay back a debt he felt he'd owed since 1950. In that year he'd been a young member of the Minnesota Air National Guard. When the Korean War broke out, members of the unit drew straws to see who would go to war and who would stay home. Eelkema drew the straw that kept him home, but he always felt guilty about it. So in 1961, as soon as he'd earned his medical degree in Seattle, he joined the uniformed public health service run by the Navy. Following his pediatrics residency at Fort Defiance on the Navajo Reservation in Arizona, he became part of the Epidemiological Intelligence Service out of Atlanta, Georgia. After undertaking encephalitis and polio surveillance in several cities, he was assigned to investigate the spread of equine influenza. This task, in which his prior experience as a veterinarian came in handy, required him to travel to various race tracks in the country. It marked the beginning of a life-long fascination with racing and betting the ponies. "I got kind of hooked on the track."

After his stint in the service, Eelkema thought he'd settle down into family practice. He hooked up with a doctor in Snohomish, Washington, and was pretty sure he'd spend the rest of his life there. But he couldn't find anything bigger than a two-bedroom house for his family of five children. In the meantime, his partner, who was strapped for cash, would pull Eelkema aside and say things like, "Don't tell that mother she's got small tonsils, we may have to take 'em out next week."

A new disillusionment set in. "I needed to re-examine my life after that," he says. "So I went camping. We spent three weeks in a tent in a state park. I stared at my navel the whole time and I decided that kind of medicine wasn't what I wanted."

In 1964 he came back to Grand Forks, out of work and unsure of what he would do. He was nearly broke and had no prospects. But in the serendipity that is so typical of his life, he found himself walking down the street in Grand Forks one day, where he spied Wally Wasdahl, the chairman of the pathology department at the medical school. When Wasdahl found out Eelkema was unemployed, he told him the school needed a student health doctor. Eelkema talked to Dean Harwood, who immediately hired him to teach physiology half-time and to run the student health service the other half.

He did that until 1967, when again he felt as if he was getting nowhere. Since he had two years of a preventive medicine residency from his naval service and needed only an academic year to get his board certification in preventive medicine. He decided to resign from UND and attend the University of California at Berkeley. "It was probably the best thing I ever did."

At the end of his training in 1968 he got a phone call from Dean Harwood back in Grand Forks. He wanted to start a public health department and wanted Eelkema to come back and head it. It sounded good. Harwood then asked him what he wanted to be called.

"I said, 'How does chairman and professor sound?' He said, 'It sounds good to me.'" And so it was, although when he got back to Grand Forks he found more than a little jealousy among long-time faculty. He hadn't gone through all the steps from instructor through assistant professor to professor. Typical of Eelkema, he laughed it off.

Still, he had one more epiphany in store for him, perhaps the most important of all. Certainly, without it, everything would have turned out differently.

It happened the year after Eelkema returned to UND. He attended a meeting of the American Public Health Association in Philadelphia, and stayed at the Belleview Stratford Hotel (where a mysterious outbreak of something called Legionnaire's Disease would rock the public health world in 1976). While there he ran into a friend from his days in the Public Health Service. Dick Smith was just getting on an elevator when Eelkema hailed him and asked what he was doing these days.

"I'm working with MEDEX," he said.

"What in the hell is MEDEX?" asked Eelkema.

As the elevator doors closed, Smith thrust a business card at him. "Call me in Seattle and we'll talk."

When he called a few days later, Smith told him that MEDEX stood for Medical Extension. It was a start-up federal program aimed at making use of the unique experience of military corpsmen. During the Vietnam War, hundreds of young men had been trained to function as independent duty corpsmen and many had seen more trauma than most doctors see in a lifetime. They were coming back from service and the idea was to make use of their experience in filling the gaps in rural areas where there weren't enough doctors to go around.

"That's what we need here in North Dakota," said Eelkema. Smith told him if he could get the support of the North Dakota Medical Association and the medical school, he'd help him start a MEDEX program in Grand Forks. At the time, only the University of Washington and Dartmouth had such programs. North Dakota, said Smith, could become the Midwest anchor for MEDEX.

Without realizing it, Eelkema had launched himself into the

world of medical politics. It didn't take him long to understand that the North Dakota Medical Association was divided into nine regions. Each region had a councilor appointed to a board of councilors that made all the decisions on behalf of the group.

"I figured I only had to get five of them behind me," he says. He began working on doctors who liked the MEDEX idea and who had agreed to help train the corpsmen when it came time. At a critical meeting of the Board of Councilors, four members voted against it, but the other five liked the idea. With the Medical Association now behind it, Dean Harwood quickly added his support. Eelkema flew to Seattle to meet with Dick Smith and write up a boilerplate application for funding. He then hand-carried it to the Bethesda, Maryland, office of Paul Sanazaro, the director of the brand-new Department of Health Manpower Research within the National Institutes of Health.

While there, Eelkema made another important connection. He shook hands with a federal administrator named Doug Fenderson, who would oversee the MEDEX program. It didn't take Eelkema long to learn that Fenderson, by happenstance, was a native of Streeter, North Dakota. The two men hit it off immediately.

"I was at a meeting in Washington with Bob and Dick Smith and a man from Dartmouth," Fenderson recalls. "Paul Sanazaro said we have research money, so submit your application. Eelkema stood up unceremoniously and said, 'That's the end of that. We're not interested in research. It takes too much time and the outcomes are too uncertain. Besides, it takes money to have a staff to prepare applications, so count me out.' He was about to walk out the door.

"Sanazaro said, 'Oh no, don't do that. We'll set up a special review for you. Fenderson here will help with the applications. We'll do whatever we can do to help you along.'"

Fenderson recalls that he himself was new to Sanazaro's office and was pleasantly surprised by Eelkema's little tantrum. "I saw it as sign of strength," he says. "I appreciated his directness and I shared much of his skepticism about research projects. I also realized the purpose of MEDEX had to do with the availability of health care in low-access areas. What could be lower access than North Dakota?

"Eelkema had, of course, been following this and wanted the North Dakota program to be a training program. Since he was already down the road on that one, he was well qualified to move. Eelkema was very straightforward and honest and matter of fact about all — it all fit into right categories."

And that's how Bob Eelkema returned to Grand Forks with $1.7 million in his pocket. He was met with a peculiar welcome. Tom Clifford, his old handball partner and now vice president of finance, clapped an arm around his shoulder.

"Geez, Bob," he said, "the university's boiler just blew up. It's gonna cost $100,000 for a new one. This grant of yours came in the nick of time. We didn't know where we were going to get the money."

Since the grant technically allowed for discretion in spending, Eelkema agreed. Informed of the generosity of Dr. Eelkema, the university's president, George Starcher, looked puzzled.

He said, "Who the hell is Eelkema?"

That's when it became apparent that Dean Harwood, in his haste to hire a chairman and professor of community medicine, had neglected to send the proper paperwork through the administrative channels. Though he'd been operating as chair of the department for some months, officially Eelkema didn't exist. And so it was that Starcher had to go before the state Board of Higher Education and ask for permission to officially hire the man who had just landed the largest grant in the history of the state.

Moses Shows the Way

5

In the meantime, Dr. Willard Wright, one of the early champions of the MEDEX program, was working closely with the University in his new position as head of the Regional Medical Program.

That program had an interesting history, dating back to when President Lyndon Johnson appointed a commission on heart, cancer and stroke, chaired by Michael DeBakey, the famed Houston heart surgeon. DeBakey's idea was that there should be centers of excellence established across the United States, each built around an existing medical school and university hospital. The most difficult cases would be handled in those centers of excellence. Naturally, the number one center was going to be in Houston.

But at the AMA, where Willard Wright was a leading officer, doctors in general were skeptical about the program. It seemed to be allocating too much power in the hands of a very few. They decided a better program would feature a diffusion of support throughout every area of the country. Each local group would be given an opportunity to develop programs and show what it could do to improve the quality of health care for all the people in their area.

That concept is roughly what got through the U.S. Congress. The Regional Medical Program law set up a very loose structure in which grants were to be made to acceptable organizations within each state, or in some cases a city or a given area. Following this legislation, various organizations applied for grants and set up their structure to operate. The North Dakota State Medical Association applied for funds to form a nonprofit organization — The NIH — distinct from the association, but controlled by it. This organization put the responsibility for better health care squarely in the laps of the doctors. They now had to prove that they could develop a program that would be of benefit to all the people, not necessarily a benefit for just the doctors.

When Wright became the first head of North Dakota's Regional Medical Program, his main objective was to improve the ongoing training of doctors. That goal brought him frequently to Grand Forks and regular contact with the School of Medicine — and in particular with the department of community medicine. Bob Eelkema's MEDEX program fit perfectly with Wright's vision of what the NIH was all about. He set out to help Eelkema locate doctors who could act as preceptors — essentially hands-on mentors — to train and oversee the new physician assistants coming out of MEDEX. At the same time, Wright acted as a bridge between the medical school and North Dakota Medical Association, lining up support across the nine regions of the association for the MEDEX program.

So it was that the brain trust of Wright, Eelkema, Nelson and Vennes were working together on a fairly regular basis when the news began trickling in about trouble with future transfers from the two-year school to established four-year programs. It was Nelson who brought that matter to a head at a January 1971 meeting of the curriculum committee, chaired by Vennes. In fact, Nelson moved that the committee investigate the possibility of establishing a four-year curriculum.

It was the first time since Harwood had arrived in 1953 that the idea of a four-year school had been formally raised. The dean was immediately opposed to the idea, but the others liked the notion of at least studying the possibility. It was either that, it seemed, or prepare to close the school.

Still, Harwood walked out of the meeting, clearly upset. In coming weeks and months he didn't try to block the investigation, but neither did he do very much to support it.

The root of his objection hadn't changed in eighteen years. He felt he understood a medical reality that others did not. In the 1930s and 1940s, North Dakota still had lots of doctors in its small towns. They were the Norman Rockwell-style GPs who practiced out of a bag and made house calls. For the most part they treated symptoms rather than making a diagnosis. It was a medical treatment that became outdated after the war as more educated physicians emerged from medical schools. Once sophisticated diagnostic equipment became available, doctors decided they couldn't be spending their days traipsing around the countryside if they were going to serve as many patients as possible. Treatment soon revolved around medical centers. But in the smaller towns, when the old-time doctors died out, people felt they were being cheated because they didn't have a doctor or a medical center. In a sense, that's what led to the mill levy in North Dakota. Many people thought that by providing more financial support to the medical school, more doctors would emerge to settle in their small towns. It's why the State Legislature voted to establish a four-year school in 1953.

In Harwood's mind, both legislative actions were well meaning, but both actually depended upon something North Dakota didn't have.

The traditional model of a four-year medical school in Harwood's day was built around a bustling university medical center. Sometimes referred to as a tertiary care hospital, the university center was where patients came after their primary care doctor and their local hospital realized they didn't have the expertise or equipment to resolve their illness. There was no such hospital in North Dakota — and even if the state could have afforded the multiple millions of dollars to build one, there was no teeming population center big enough to provide a daily stream of cases on which medical students could practice and learn.

So Harwood kept sidestepping the four-year idea, while the state's Board of Medical Examiners tried strategy after strategy to induce more doctors to come into the state. None was very successful.

By then, in the late 1950s and into the 1960s, the trend in medical education had shifted toward specialties. At about the same time, most infectious diseases began to disappear. Doctors were handed new tools that made a tremendous difference in the amount of diseases and types of diseases they could treat. But these tools required highly technical and expensive procedures and a lot more training. To support this, the federal government was pouring huge sums of money into education and research. Many educators feared that everything was being geared toward making a doctor more of a technician than a compassionate human being. In that world, the university hospital center was king, even though across the country people still wanted one friendly doctor to treat their whole family.

A shift, which Harwood might not have fully appreciated, took place in 1965 with the passage of Medicare and Medicaid. Huge sums of federal money suddenly became available for basic treatment, as opposed to research. As cats follow catnip, the emphasis of medical education suddenly moved to treatment. Now government planners began to have a great fear that there weren't going to be enough doctors to handle all of it. Soon politicians, reacting to the pressures from their constituents, began pushing educators and medical groups to develop new medical schools and new ways of using such schools to educate physicians for the needs of the patient and not the doctor.

The educators were stunned at the turnaround. They didn't know whether to build more medical schools with the structure of a university hospital, or somehow return to the century-old model based on the mentor-preceptor. In fact, the time was suddenly right for experimentation with new models of medical training. To an old-school administrator like Harwood, that must have seemed an incredible leap. Ironically, though, everything he had done to beef up the staffing at the two-year school during his tenure provided it with the perfect flexibility to expand when the time came. Had he been a bad dean, the proposed expansion to a four-year school would have cost much more than it eventually did and might have died in committee.

Once the vote to investigate the options had passed that meeting of John Vennes's curriculum committee in Grand Forks, things began to move very quickly.

To a man like Willard Wright, it seemed obvious that it would be easier to develop a completely new school around the two-year program than to start from scratch. He was particularly encouraged because in recent years in North Dakota a cadre of doctors had been educating themselves on the ins and outs of organization. These were doctors who, like Wright, had served on committees of the Medical Association, on the research foundation, on the association council. They had become leaders of their profession, people who had been working together for several years and who had developed a certain ability to get things done. It seemed to Wright that all they needed now was the right challenge to motivate them.

The challenge he had in mind was daunting. What was needed was a totally different concept from that of any other medical school in the country. If there was no single institution in the state large enough to support medical students, then perhaps the medical school should go in a completely new direction. Why not farm the

students out to smaller communities where established doctors —
preceptors, mentors — would train them on behalf of the medical
school in the course of their daily work?

Was that possible?

One thing Wright knew perhaps better than anyone: if it could
work, the state's doctors would have to be completely behind it.
Without their support, the medical school was going nowhere.

Wright undertook a "quick and dirty" mail survey of the state's
doctors to test the waters. He learned that nobody was dissatisfied
with the quality of the first two years at UND's School of Medicine. In
fact, he found a great deal of pride in the basic science program at
UND. The vast majority wanted to see the school continue to thrive
and not disband. Wright also asked doctors if they would be interested in lending their expertise to teach medical students in a decen-
tralized medical school. Again, the overwhelming majority said yes.

The enthusiasm of their responses bolstered the morale of the
men of the curriculum committee. Wright then proposed the next
step. What was needed, he said, was someone to perform an outside,
independent study of the entire medical school question. Without it,
the doctors wouldn't formally agree to anything. Without the formal
backing of doctors, state legislators who controlled the budget
wouldn't even consider an expansion plan.

Because Wright had such high-placed connections in the AMA, he
felt confident he could persuade a colleague with the right credentials to undertake the study. He was disappointed, however, when
everyone he approached was too busy to help out. There was
another problem as well. Even if they could help, he had no money
in his NIH budget to pay them. Normally, funding for such a study
might come from the budget of the medical school itself. But an
unconvinced Harwood wouldn't spring for a dime.

Again, Eelkema and his fat MEDEX grant came to the rescue. On
the spot, he agreed to give Wright, as head of the Regional Medical
Program, $38,000 to hire an expert. "This was totally illegal," says

Eelkema today. "We figured it would be easier to apologize than to ask permission. Besides, we had the money and we needed to do something for this medical school."

He ended up justifying the expenditure with the vague explanation that NIH had been hired to provide MEDEX services. "I hope," he says now, "that the people that do the audit on MEDEX, if it ever comes to that thirty years later, will not fault me for using that money for that kind of a purpose."

At any rate, MEDEX took care of the money part of the problem. There were two other issues to resolve. First, the state Medical Association had to be persuaded that a feasibility study was even needed. But as for the expert to do the study, Eelkema had just the man in mind. His name was Gary Dunn and things were about to get really interesting.

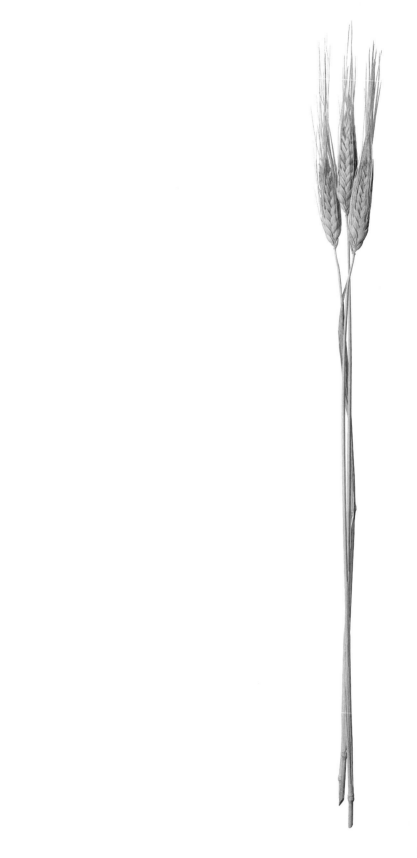

The Lovable Fraud

6

No one who examines the School of Medicine at the University of North Dakota could ignore the role Gary Dunn played — though there are many who would prefer to forget him completely. Not possible. At the very least, the controversial name of Gary Dunn is attached to one of the most significant reports ever written about the needs of the medical school — a report that played the central role in 1972 in keeping the school alive and headed for a brighter future.

But be warned, says Dr. Bill Harlan.

"Everything you hear about Gary Dunn will be one of two extremes," he says. "There's nothing in between about him. He was one of the most fascinating people I've ever met. I don't usually like sociopaths, but I think Gary was a sociopath. Yet Gary was also a leprechaun. There was something magical about him. I'll just say point blank — I don't think they could have done it without Gary being there."

Harlan, a former UND consultant who now does work for the

National Institute of Mental Health, is right about extremes. In Bismarck, for example, Dick Davison, the likable and easygoing former executive director of the state Board of Higher Education, goes rigid when asked about Dunn.

"Gary Dunn had a silk tongue," he says in disgust. "He was a crooked son-of-a-bitch."

Hearing that, Tom Clifford can only smile.

"Gary Dunn was an enigma," he says. "He was a smart guy and a fraud. He misrepresented his credentials. But he was a lovable fraud. And he had a golden set of guts. He was a real infighter and I liked him."

Much of what is known about Dunn comes from what the man himself claimed, and even his friends say a good bit of that is suspect. How much is authentic not even they are sure. Dunn died of brain cancer in 1984, and today even his widow, Nancy Dunn, admits to a conflict of emotions about him.

"He was the funniest man I ever met," she recalled recently. "The brightest and undoubtedly the most complex. Was he honest? He thought he was an honest person. He was true to his own set of values. They wouldn't always be someone else's. I think sometimes he would see something sooner than others and before long he would have convinced himself of it so he would be speaking from something he believed in, even though it didn't exist in other people's reality."

What is indisputable about Dunn was his appearance. At 5-11, the former college linebacker was squarely built, with broad shoulders, a strong jaw line and, from several different observers, the possessor of "twinkly blue eyes."

"He liked to tell people he was half-Irish and half-Jewish," recalls Nancy Dunn, "half of which was true."

His taste in clothing was remarkable in its studied informality. When the governor of Alabama invited him to his inaugural ball, Dunn showed up wearing a black tuxedo and black Converse tennis shoes. Often he wore flowered coveralls at work.

He was born in Oakland, California, claimed to have graduated from Stanford, but both Nancy Dunn and Clifford say that was a lie. He studied in Canada, apparently earned a legitimate master's degree, and told people he'd been the superintendent of a California school district in his twenties.

It was at the University of Alabama in 1970 that Bill Harlan first met Dunn. Harlan was a cardiologist who had fled into academics, disillusioned at the bureaucratic government hassles that went with practicing medicine. He'd blossomed in academia as a gifted organizer and had been recruited to Alabama as an associate dean for family practice and primary care. One of his jobs was to put together a MEDEX program, much like the one at the Veterans Hospital in Seattle run by Bob Eelkema's friend, Dick Smith.

The dean of the medical school at Alabama told Harlan he ought to speak with Gary Dunn, a man recently hired away from the Seattle MEDEX program.

"I found Gary charming but with a lot of ideas," recalls Harlan. "He'd say you've got to think outside the box. I was resistant to it. I'd met other charming people and was skeptical. Then I sort of watched Gary operate. He knew a lot of people. They all said the same thing. He's got a lot of good ideas, but what does he do?"

Actually, says Harlan, Dunn didn't seem to have a real job at Alabama — or a life. He practically lived out of his office at the university. Once the dean had introduced him to Harlan, Dunn latched onto him and seemed to do nothing else.

He'd been married and divorced some years back in California, and was the father of five children. His secretary from Seattle MEDEX days, then Nancy Hepburn, visited regularly in Birmingham. Gary had developed a regular circuit of consulting, flying back and forth between Seattle, North Dakota, Dartmouth and Birmingham.

"He fairly liberally took time to go out on his consulting visits," says Harlan. "He never took a leave of absence from Alabama. Things were free and loose in those days. Medical schools were doing well and seldom looked behind the bill to find out who was paying and how much they were paying."

To Harlan and others, Dunn always seemed to have unlimited means. He was quick to pick up a check at dinner and seemed to be independently wealthy, or at least a man who was pulling down a hefty salary. Neither was true. Dunn was always in money trouble, a man who borrowed heavily from friends to repay debts to other friends, though he took pains to keep that from public view.

His connection to North Dakota was as serendipitous as Bob Eelkema's connection to Dick Smith — the Seattle doctor who'd shoved his MEDEX business card at Bob through those closing elevator doors. In 1970, as Eelkema was trying to establish a MEDEX curriculum to train ex-military corpsmen as physicians' assistants, he was in frequent contact with Smith. UND was the second program in the country to start a MEDEX class and had lots of grant money.

"But we didn't know exactly what to teach," says Eelkema. "We were told by Dick Smith that someone named Gary Dunn, who had helped develop the MEDEX curriculum in Washington, was an educational expert. He was now associate dean for allied health down at the University of Alabama. We invited Gary up and he had a lot of really pertinent things to say about education. He really impressed me with his ideas."

In fact, Eelkema and Dunn hit it off immediately. Both were blustery, expansive types given to rolling laughter; neither was bound by decorum, let alone rules. The two men might hatch an idea about a new medical curriculum and impulsively hop on an airplane to Washington or Denver in search of funding. Always, it was Eelkema's MEDEX grant money paying the way. As an added spice, both were serious devotees of horse racing.

"Bob was Gary's best friend and Gary was Bob's best friend," says Nancy. "They went everywhere together."

"He was just a fun guy to be with," says Eelkema. "He didn't have an M.D. but he was smarter than most M.D.s. We used to drink

64

together. He was Irish, full of blarney, but he was likable. He was spontaneous, like me. He was also an imposter. Whether he had the education he claimed, or not, I'm not sure. He always claimed to have been in the Korean War. He was probably never even in the military. Some people, if they say something enough times, they end up believing it. Gary was kind of like that. He kind of built a life for himself by just imagining it.

"He would tell the story about the guy driving a one-ton truck with two tons of chickens in the back. Every so often the guy'd stop and rap on the back of the truck. He said, 'I'm trying to keep one ton in the air at all times.' That was Gary. His life was always one ton in the air. He lived on the edge a lot, so he had to live by his wits. He sometimes borrowed money and some people didn't get paid back. Some of them got very mad at him. I think he really intended to pay back everybody, but he just kept so many chickens in the air that he wasn't capable of doing it after he got brain cancer. But he was a good guy, anyway."

One of the people he borrowed from and didn't repay was Bill Harlan, the man he persuaded to go with him on his consulting trips to North Dakota.

"Oh, he told some wonderful stories," says Harlan. "He told me he'd marched across the bridge at Selma during the civil rights march of 1963. He said he'd been beaten in the back by a cop with a billy club. In the hospital he said they found a hemorrhage in his kidney. I said to him, 'Gee, usually you have to have the kidney taken out.' And he said well, they talked about it but they never did."

Harlan then asked Gary why he didn't qualify for veterans' benefits if he'd been in the Korean War. He told him he'd been in the Marine Corps, but was declared AWOL during the Korean War because of a trip to Japan. It was all a misunderstanding, he said, but he'd been given an administrative discharge. Therefore, he didn't get veterans' benefits.

"He'd never been in the Marine Corps," smiles Harlan. "Yet he really gravitated toward Clifford, the Marine."

Clifford, though, was the kind of Marine who judged a man more by his actions than by what he said.

"I don't think Gary was trained professionally or academically," he says. "He told me he went to Stanford, but he never went there. I knew that because I knew the registrar. But he was very astute and he had courage. He'd go into a room or a meeting no matter where it was or who it was, and he'd put on a front. He'd talk about the medical school and if he didn't know completely about it, he had enough information to bluff. He had the guts of a government mule. There was never a doubt in his mind that he wasn't right. We'd look at each other sometimes. And you don't like to tell a guy he's full of it. I'd look at him and I'd say, 'How is it you're thinking that way?' And he'd say, 'Well, I'm sure you know.' And I'd say, 'Yes, I know.' You see, he always knew that I knew he was a fraud. And we had a real good relationship."

So it was that Gary Dunn was the man Bob Eelkema proposed as the perfect outside expert to prepare a study about the medical school. Willard Wright agreed, with the stipulation that Dunn appear before the Regional Medical Program board to be approved. Since the North Dakota Medical Association was the sponsor of the RMP, their boards were identical. Dunn, therefore, would be appearing essentially before the leaders of the medical association.

On May 1, 1971, Eelkema brought Dunn to an association meeting in Fargo and introduced him around. It was an occasion that required not only a certain formality but the clothes to match. No longer in linebacker trim, Dunn by now was rotund, bordering on fat. He showed up in the only professional suit he owned, a tight-fitting, three-piece number, bursting at the seams, its buttons threatening to pop off every time he took a breath. But what he lacked in sartorial impressiveness, he made up for in the elaborate, free-wheeling presentation he made to the board. They were duly impressed by the depth of the man's knowledge, though Eelkema recalls it was a classic Gary Dunn performance, long on style, short on substance.

At the end of the meeting, the board agreed that they did need a feasibility study to determine whether the medical school should expand to a four-year degree granting program. They further agreed to give the job of preparing the balanced and very objective study to Gary Dunn.

The Fort Wayne Pistons

7

Of course, there was no way that Gary Dunn, especially in the company of his sidekick Bob Eelkema, was going to be objective. From the very beginning, the two worked as a tag team, traveling together, always conspiring on how to stack the deck in favor of a four-year school.

While air travel, even to places like Bismarck, was almost unknown to faculty at the cost-conscious university, it became routine for the Dunn/Eelkema project to fly off to meeting after meeting. As usual, commercial flights and fees to cover the use of university planes were paid for with MEDEX funds.

"The grant money greased the wheels," says Eelkema. "Without greasing wheels, I don't think we would have been able to do what we did. I couldn't get any travel money out of Harwood. This way we were able to just get in the plane and go. We didn't have to ask permission from anybody."

In the course of nine months they traveled to about sixty meetings across the region. They investigated South Dakota's efforts to expand its two-year school, they visited the Mayo Clinic in Rochester, Minnesota, and the University of Minnesota in Minneapolis-St. Paul. They even took an impromptu trip to Washington, D.C.

Some of the trips were made in planes owned or leased by the university. This came courtesy of John Odegard, the man who would go on to found a nationally-recognized aerospace program at the university. At the time, Odegard was in charge of a small department of aviation. He and Eelkema started at UND at about the same time and bonded when they realized they were each newcomers without portfolio. Public health, Eelkema's specialty, has never gotten the respect it deserves from other doctors. And the idea of an aviation program was easily dismissed as irrelevant in the early 1970s. In fact the faculty council at UND strongly opposed the addition of any courses in lowbrow aviation, feeling they demeaned the stature of the university. Clifford, who became a champion not only of the medical school but of the fledgling aviation department as well — and was a president who never had much use for faculty councils — got around that by creating courses called "transportation economics." The rest is history: the John Odegard School of Aerospace Studies is today an internationally acclaimed school with 1,500 students from around the world, and recognized departments in aviation education, atmospheric research, space studies, and computer science.

At any rate, Odegard was only too willing to help his friend Eelkema get wherever he needed to go. Only once did he have doubts. That was the time Dunn and Eelkema flew to Duluth in a UND plane to consult with officials at the University of Minnesota. They were scheduled to go back to Grand Forks and there take a commercial flight to Washington. The eager-to-please UND pilot supplied by Odegard told them there was no need to go all the way back to North Dakota. He could fly them to Washington right now.

It sounded so easy. But the plane was scarcely in the air when both Dunn and Eelkema realized they had a serious problem. The two had been out on the town the night before and had apparently "eaten some bad fish." They become so ill their pilot had to make an unscheduled stop in Fort Wayne, Indiana. Matters went from bad to worse. Inside the terminal in the tiny airport, Dunn and Eelkema found a men's room with coin-operated toilets only. Who has coins at a time like that? One can only wonder about the reaction the Board of Councilors of the North Dakota Medical Association might have had, watching their two experts crawling and squeezing beneath the stalls to get the relief they needed.

But the adventure wasn't quite finished. Back in the plane, the pilot admitted to his passengers as they approached the nation's Capitol that he was lost. He had no map, no flight plan. He'd never flown to Washington before. Not to worry, however. He dropped the plane down to rooftop level, spotted the Washington Monument, and flew happily on toward National Airport.

When they landed, the eyes of stunned airport officials only grew wider. The plane disembarked two passengers so wrapped in heavy winter clothing that they looked like a pair of Pillsbury Doughboys in bearskins.

Welcome to the big city, boys.

When they returned to North Dakota, a bewildered John Odegard asked Eelkema what in the world had happened. The FAA had contacted him and told him his pilot had violated almost every rule in the book. As usual, Eelkema just laughed.

In spite of such high jinks, the fact-finding trips made by Dunn and Eelkema brought back some very curious and useful information. The pair had made a point in their travels to visit doctors and clinics and ask about patient contacts. For, even though the Medical Association had approved the idea of a study, they hadn't approved the idea of an expansion. Many doctors still believed — as did Harwood — that the state just didn't have enough people to provide the cases medical students needed to train with. That argument always fed into the lack of a large, tertiary care teaching hospital.

The patient contact studies Dunn and Eelkema conducted in Minnesota showed what everyone expected: the Mayo Clinic, for example, saw 200,000 patients a year. No single hospital in North Dakota came near that many.

On the other hand, comparison studies in North Dakota surprised everyone. The two hospitals in Bismarck saw a combined 300,000 patients a year.

Eelkema immediately grasped the implications. "We said if Mayo is training 550 residents on 200,000 contacts, why couldn't we train fifty medical students on 300,000 contacts? And that didn't even include Fargo or Grand Forks. We found out that the patient encounters across the state were comparable, if not more so, than those at big teaching schools."

All they needed, Dunn told Eelkema, was an educational model to take advantage of those contacts.

In fact, they needed a lot more than that. Because it wasn't just a medical model issue and it wasn't just doctors they had to convince. There was the little matter of the North Dakota Legislature. That was going to require muscle of a different kind.

Like, for instance, the kind of muscle that showed up on campus the day Gary Dunn moved in. He and Nancy had rented an apartment in Grand Forks in a building that had once been the dormitory of the nursing school, across from the main campus. The hallways were very narrow, and the movers who were schlepping their furniture had a difficult time maneuvering.

In the group that day were Gary and Nancy. They allowed everyone to believe they were married, for cohabitation in 1973 in North Dakota without benefit of marriage was still an eyebrow raiser, perhaps even a career-ender. Present, also, was Libby Johnson, a UND grad who was managing the move for the university.

Nancy Dunn, who has always drawn raves for her organizational skills, directed the burly movers like a drill sergeant as they negotiated those tight corners. Then came Gary's large desk and there seemed to be no way it could fit down the hallway. Nancy was more optimistic, wading into the knot of movers with suggestions of what end to grab and which way to tip it.

"All of a sudden there appeared among the movers this very strong person who just took over and made it happen," recalls Nancy. "He introduced himself to me. I thought he must be their supervisor. He said his name was Tom. Well, I wanted to introduce Libby to Tom, because she had made the move happen. Tom set the desk down and I said, 'Libby, I'd like you to meet Tom.' And by that time Libby had backed herself up against the wall and she had this look in her eye. If she'd taken one step further she would have fallen through the window. She looked at me and said, 'Nancy, I know who he is.'"

Of course, "he" was Tom Clifford. The hands-on president who had just taken office, and knew from his handball partner Bob Eelkema that the Dunns had moved to town and might need some help.

It was in the steam rooms just off the university's old handball courts that Eelkema had been keeping Clifford up to date on the looming crisis in the medical school. In those six months before Clifford officially took office, he had learned about the transfer problems, the need for a feasibility study and the very creative hiring of Gary Dunn.

The more he heard about their fact-finding trips, the more Clifford realized it was about time for him to step in and take part in the enterprise. For as much as the doctors needed convincing, the final battle over expanding the medical school or killing it outright was going to be fought on the floor of the North Dakota State Legislature.

Imperial Cass

8

Clifford had learned well from John West how to get along with the crowd in Bismarck. He knew almost every legislator by name and what's more, he even liked most of them. They knew that and repaid the favor by giving him pretty much what he'd asked for at budget time in his days as vice-president for finance. In Clifford they saw a glimpse of themselves. That's probably because Clifford was such a good listener and made them feel important. He was the kind of leader they wanted to become.

"Leadership is ephemeral," he says today. "It's a lot of traits. I don't know if it's taught or you're born with it. There're some big theories about that, but I think it's part of each. I think you have some personal instincts that help you become a leader. But I always liked people. I think that's part of being a leader — trying to find a way to help them. At the same time, though, when it comes to brass tacks, it's put up or shut up. You have to be tough enough to do that."

Yet even as they respected and liked Clifford, and had treated him easily in the past, the North Dakota State Legislature, as cost conscious as they come, was not about to roll over and wag its tail at the prospect of spending $3 million on the medical school. He had his work cut out for him.

Legislative observers recall that in the early 1970s there was tremendous competition for every state-provided dollar. In fact, that's true almost any year in North Dakota, a fiscally conservative state where even the rare liberals hate to spend money. And when the legislature does vote to spend money, the voters have a chance to say no you don't. Bryce Streibel, the Fessenden Republican who was floor leader of the state's House of Representatives in the 1971–73 Legislature, recalls the year 1987 when ten different spending plans were referred for public vote in a special election.

"Now these were issues the Legislature had already passed," emphasizes the proudly conservative Streibel. "And they were all thrown out. When you think of the electorate today, it's a tragedy voters don't spend more time thinking about what government is all about, and what paths are laid down for them and what legacy they are going to leave for the generations to follow. You can't just say that because something costs money it's no good. But too many people do."

Evan Lips, the Bismarck Republican who served more than thirty years in the State Senate, remembers the day in 1989 when a rural legislator stood up in a budget committee hearing and asked, "Why do we educate our young anyway? They just move away." Lips remembers the squelch he put on the man. "What do you want us to do — send them out dumb?"

Just so, the early 1970s weren't much different. Earl Strinden, another conservative stalwart of the House in those days, representing Grand Forks, says, "There was no question about it. There were those who just believed North Dakota could no longer afford a medical school. The big issue was the cost. After all, when you take the budget of the medical school, it exceeds the budget of some of our smaller colleges. You say, 'How many students? My God, eighty students! And for God's sakes we're operating Mayville College for half that and they've got 600 students.' Those are real questions and many of us were concerned about it. Could we offer a quality four-year program? Do we have the population base? The diversity of patient load? Would we be able to give a good quality education? Would our graduates be on the level of graduates of established medical schools? After all, if you're training in Cook County Hospital in Chicago, you're going to have experiences that you're never going to have in Carrington, North Dakota."

Clifford had heard the arguments and knew it wouldn't be an easy fight. Which is why he'd begun laying careful plans to present the medical school as an investment North Dakota had to make in its future. He went to work on his strategy more than a year before the issue would come before the State Legislature. And while his intention was to appeal to everyone in the state, in many ways his plan could have been called the Fargo gambit.

Long-suffering North Dakotans are used to the ignorant slight given them by outsiders who know little about the state, and believe Fargo is the be-all and end-all. First there was both a boxer and a movie called "The Fargo Express." Then came the Sesame Street character "Fargo North, Decoder." Most recently, the nation saw the Cohen brothers' quirky movie *Fargo* (which really had more to do with quirkiness among Minnesotans).

The thing is, it's not just outsiders who think that way.

"Sometimes, in North Dakota," opines Emerson Murray, the wizened old veteran of the Legislative Council who hails from Rugby, "it's said we have Fargo and the rest of North Dakota."

Years ago some wag coined the term Imperial Cass, to refer to the high-sniffing attitude some perceive from the county that contains Fargo. It's often said by people from Minot, for example, or Williston that from Fargo you can't see the rest of North Dakota. Feathers are also ruffled west of the Red River about the way power brokers in Fargo seem to think they are the power brokers of the state as well.

That rivalry was evident in 1971. Fargo in those days was the state's largest and wealthiest city, and home to UND's arch enemy on any athletic field, North Dakota State University. It was said then — and is oft repeated today — that someone who grew up in one of the two city's couldn't help but hate the other. Fargo also represented a perfect example of what the medical profession had devolved into. Two private clinics there controlled most of the medical treatment in the city. Those clinics were teeming with specialists and sub-specialists, high powered, highly paid doctors who had been trained in large tertiary care hospitals and who thought the idea of training medical students anywhere else was ridiculous.

But it wasn't just their opinion that concerned Clifford and other proponents of a four-year medical school. It was the political clout they carried, and frequently flexed, to back up their beliefs. Again, this was no mere perception. It was as real as the personage of C. Warner Litten, the majority leader of the State Senate who, as it happened, also was the administrator of the largest of the two Fargo clinics. He had tremendous influence among the city's medical community — and vice versa. It was the doctors he worked for, Litten says, who had approached him years earlier and asked him to run for state office to protect their interests.

In other parts of the state, specialists were less common; opinion on a medical school expansion, if not favorable, was at least less hostile. But even mid-state fence-straddlers came under heavy pressure from the Fargo contingent, which enlisted the support of those legislators across the state who saw cost and only cost as the singular criterion for voting most measures up or down.

"I was admonished hundreds of times," says Streibel, "that we were foolhardy even to waste our time trying to get a four-year medical school — by legislators, doctors and taxpayers from Fargo and elsewhere. I remember it went like this: 'The legislators who support that and vote for it, well they better enjoy their session, because it's going to be the last one.' You'd hear that at meetings even in your own districts."

Earl Strinden felt the same heat. "There were partisan aspects where some people in Fargo felt if they could bring this medical school down to ashes, they could rebuild from the ashes a new medical school and have it located there, rather than in Grand Forks. You had medical people with strong egos. Smart people pretty convinced in their own minds that they knew what was right."

Add to the bubbling caldron this spice from Murray:

"In the legislative process in North Dakota," he says, "all that the opponents of a bill have to show is that the proponents are divided among themselves. And then?" (He makes a sharp cutting motion across his throat.) "You're done. So you've got to go to the Legislature with a very close, very united front. There are always legislators who just aren't going to spend money on anything, practically. Now, we want people like that, because they put budgets to the test. But sometimes the answer should come out yes. So it was important that Tom and his group show unity."

But as long as there was a Fargo, how was that even remotely possible?

In a way it sounded as formidable as, well, as attacking a cliff with tanks. Which was Tom Clifford's cue to enter, stage left.

Although the job description for the president of the University of North Dakota said nothing about being a politician, in reality much of the work of the university was conducted in the political arena. Clifford, as we have seen, was adept at politics. But as an old football player, he also knew the value of teamwork, and his favorite play was the end run. There would be a time for stepping squarely into the arena. In the meantime, he was happy to work the perimeter, setting up his play.

"Oh, I suppose I was a little bit of a politician," Clifford says today with an impish grin. Indeed. The state's Republicans thought so much of his skills that they begged him several times to run for statewide office. During his years as president he delivered 100 speeches a year across the state and had an eighty-seven per cent name recognition — higher than the governor. When Republican Governor Edward Schafer was elected in 1993, he appointed Clifford as head of his transition team. But his supporters howled. "You can't do that," they said. "He's a Democrat."

The thing is, nobody really knew what Clifford was, which is the way he intended it.

"I played the middle ground," he says. "You have to. My tendencies have been toward the Democratic platform but my association has been primarily with Republicans in business. I think I'm a little more compassionate than some of those guys are. We're a very unconventional group in North Dakota. Here we are, as conservative as you can get. Yet through the influence of the Scandinavian culture, we're also more cooperative. I found a very old letter once in the university archives from a guy from Boston who came out here. He was writing back to his brother. The gist of it was: 'What a hell of a country. The rivers run north and the Irish vote Republican.'"

When it came down to it, Clifford resisted all overtures to run for office. "I didn't want to run for governor or Congress and I'll tell you why. I didn't want to kiss people's backsides to get things done. I saw what they had to do and I didn't want to compromise that."

Yet it was going to take a very smooth, a very slick politician to win this fight. Even Clifford's friends wondered if he was up to the task. They all knew that the no-compromise, no-butt-kissing variety of politics was as rare in these parts as a Club Med tourist.

The Fessenden Cabal

9

To the uninitiated, it might seem that the best way to get a bill introduced into the State Legislature is to wait until the session starts, approach a few carefully selected representatives and senators, take them to dinner and lobby your case. Many inexperienced proponents of legislation do just that and are sorely disappointed when they can't seem to get those key legislators to focus on their particular cause. No matter how fancy the dinner.

There are a couple of realities that the inexperienced do not take into consideration. First, in North Dakota the legislature meets only in odd-numbered years. This fits the nature of life in the state, where most lawmakers have businesses or farms or ranches to run. When all those legislators finally do descend on Bismarck, there's suddenly about eighteen months worth of new issues to catch up on. Every person who came up with an idea in that interim between sessions is now standing at your door with an expectant smile.

"The Legislature is a pressure cooker, that's the only way to describe their work," says Em Murray, the former head of the Legislative Council. "There is just no way you can take on big projects from ground zero during the legislative session. You can't do it because you just can't get enough understanding. North Dakotans in the Legislature range from middle of the road to conservative in the main. They won't gamble very much."

Another, perhaps surprising fact of life: buying a legislator dinner isn't necessarily going to get you very far in North Dakota.

"When my father found out I was running for the State Legislature," recalls Bryce Streibel, the House majority leader in 1973, "he said, 'Kid, if you're ever stupid enough to sell your soul for a buck, be damn sure the price tag is high enough, because there's only one sale.' Boy, is that true. Some people can be bought for a martini and a steak. But once bought, you're bought forever."

"Basically," adds Murray, "the Legislature is made up of honorable people who work for the public first. The person who is working for his own ego or aggrandizement sooner or later oversteps himself and is not too effective. Gradually, he loses the thing he's working for. Salt of the earth is an exaggeration, but there's an element of truth in it out here, doggone it. People do come to Bismarck to work for the public good. They certainly don't come here for the money. They are not overpaid by any means."

Another intriguing element about North Dakota politics in the early 1970s was the almost dignified way it was usually practiced. "You could be quite vigorously opposed to an adversary but there was always an undercurrent of respect there," says former Governor Art Link. "For the most part, politicians remain friends in North Dakota. I think it comes from our close ethnic backgrounds. Political persuasion doesn't cause you not to be neighborly."

As proof, Link, a life-long Democrat, was elected to the U.S. Congress in 1970 largely with the support of Bryce Streibel, the classic conservative Republican. Nothing unusual about that, says Streibel, the former undertaker from Fessenden.

"When it comes to a decision of supporting a candidate with

ethics and integrity versus one who has none, party loyalty takes a back seat," Streibel wrote in his autobiography, *Pathways Through Life*. "But you better believe the wrath of hundreds of hard core ... Republicans was upon me."

In that spirit of collegiality, says Streibel today, "I think the most rewarding experience of anyone who holds elective office is to look at your counterpart across the political aisle with a degree of camaraderie and friendship. There is nothing more rewarding than to pass some major legislation with both parties involved. But so few people see that. If it's just Republicans sponsoring a bill, well, number one, you're looking at a big hurdle immediately. If the bill does pass, there's no rewarding experience to it. When you get both sides voting for it and it passes, you feel good."

However, North Dakota legislators weren't always so amicable. In the years before 1947, the intense pressures of the short legislative session caused such bickering and fighting among legislators that there was concern about the quality of work being accomplished. Members of one party wouldn't be caught dead having lunch with someone from a rival party. According to Murray, the legislative sessions in the first half of the twentieth century were a jumble of "numerous committees meeting from periods as short as an hour — with overlapping membership and quorum problems — in every nook and cranny where a meeting could be held. Consequently, legislators were unable to take anything but a shallow approach to the measures that were placed before them, and largely from sources outside ... "

But in 1947 the Legislature created the Legislative Council. It was to streamline and organize the entire process of researching and drafting bills, establishing committees and scheduling meetings. The Council is run by an executive director, but it works directly for a committee of legislators, including eight members of the House of Representatives — four from each party — and seven members of the Senate — four from the majority party. Those fifteen elect a chairman, who has tremendous power over which issues will come up for deliberation in the next legislative sessions. Traditionally, the chairman appoints various committees to work during the interim months between legislative sessions. Typically, these committees hold hearings, research issues and prepare a recommendation to the sitting legislature.

"As legislators started having to work together in the interim, they got to know each other," says Murray. "They were eating meals together, sometimes sharing hotel rooms as we'd hold hearings around the state. It improved the camaraderie of all legislators a great deal. They got to where they trusted each other."

That trust is even quantifiable. Whereas barely fifty per cent of all bills introduced by individual legislators ever pass, says Murray, those bills sponsored or endorsed by the Legislative Council have anywhere from an eighty per cent to almost a 100 per cent chance of passage.

"In those days," says Murray, "if you could get the leadership of the Council committed in support of a bill, you really had a leg up. I know that's what Tom Clifford was thinking when he flew into Fessenden."

It was seven miles east of Fessenden, in Wells County near the center of the state, that Bryce Streibel was born in 1922. His grandfather, Heinrich Streibel, had begun the family homestead in 1889, raising wheat on 120 of his 140 acres in Germantown Township. Like Reinhold, his father, Bryce Streibel was educated in a one-room school house in Germantown, though he later graduated from Fessenden High School. His early memories are of life in the Depression. "And I mean it was a sucker," he says. "No crops, just grasshoppers and Russian thistles. Our allowance was a penny a week. All I can remember is no money. But the work ethic, that was there."

It helped him work his way through the University of North Dakota, where he played on the football team and met a young man named Tom Clifford.

"I knew him pretty well," says Clifford. "He was a tireless worker. And he was hardnosed. If he told you he'd do something, he'd do it."

Streibel headed west as a young man. In California he met his future wife, June, and worked as a design engineer and as a funeral home operator. He came back to North Dakota to run the family farm when his father, a long-time state senator, fell ill.

In 1956, Streibel took up the political mantle of his father and was elected as a state representative from the 33rd Legislative District. A fervent Republican, he began moving up the ladder. Though he ran unsuccessfully for lieutenant governor in 1960, his career in the House eventually landed him the powerful job of majority floor leader. (In the North Dakota House of Representatives, the grander title of Speaker of the House is mostly ceremonial. The real power lies in the hands of the majority leader.)

In 1971, when Tom Clifford boarded a university plane to fly down to Fessenden to see his old college friend, Bryce Streibel was one of the most powerful men in North Dakota. Not only was he the leading Republican in the House, he was also the chairman of the all-important Legislative Council. If he liked your idea, it was a very good thing.

Clifford hoped Streibel liked the idea of a four-year medical school. He hoped he would be amenable to what he was about to ask him. But, of course, he wouldn't simply pick up the telephone and call him.

"Oh no," says Clifford. "For one thing, Bryce liked the idea that he was important enough that the president of the university came to his house all the way to Fessenden. I used to do that a lot. North Dakota people don't like to have you call them in. They don't like summonses. You go to *them*. The other thing — in this state if they ask you to do something, they want you, not a delegate or a vice-president. I made over a hundred speeches a year in North Dakota. I never turned one down if I could help it. I went all over. I never sent a delegate. If I couldn't go I just said I can't make it, can you do it another day. They'd do that but they did not like to have you send someone else. I'll just tell you, that's the way we are. So I flew out there to Fessenden to see him."

Actually, the plane flew into Harvey International Airport, a grand name for the small airstrip sixteen miles up the road from Fessenden. Streibel met the plane and drove Clifford and pilot John Odegard back to his modest split-level home. The way he remembers it, his wife June fixed everyone lunch. Clifford remembers a coffee cake. Whatever it was, the two men retired to Streibel's tiny office, the smallest of three bedrooms on the second level. It's a room filled with a books and memorabilia, a desk, two chairs and a card table. It was a cozy, though somewhat unlikely place to decide the future of the School of Medicine.

For that's what it came down to.

In setting up the meeting, Clifford had given Streibel no hint about the topic. "My curiosity had already gotten the best of me," Streibel recalled in *Pathways Through Life*, "because it isn't an everyday occurrence for a university president to call upon a Wells County farmer."

At the card table, Clifford started it off: "What do you think of a four-year medical school, Bryce?"

"I don't have to think long on that," Streibel replied almost immediately. "I'm for it."

Recalling the conversation in an interview for this book, Streibel said, "I think he was kind of a little bit amazed. I have been known to be conservative. I'm conservative in certain areas. But I can be construed to be a liberal in areas that are of concern to our society."

In fact, Clifford was aware that Streibel would vote to fund strong infrastructures for the future of the state, such as dams, roads and schools. As Murray put it, "Bryce was willing to spend real money on things he felt would get a return later on."

That was key for Clifford. He told Streibel that in his strategy sessions in Grand Forks with people like Earl Strinden, the idea of selling the medical school expansion as an investment, and not just another hike in the higher education appropriation, seemed a good way to go. Streibel agreed. But it wasn't just his enthusiasm or even Streibel's support alone, that Clifford sought. He had come to Fessenden because of a metaphorical quirk about North Dakota geography. From Bryce Streibel's den window, you could very plainly see Fargo.

That's when Clifford told the chairman of the Legislative Council he wanted him to appoint a special committee to study the future of the medical school. He was doing just what Em Murray said needed to be done: trying to get that leg up on the opposition. Clifford knew that without a strong recommendation from an interim study committee, the chances for approval of a bill to expand the medical school were not good. The Fargo opposition was too formidable. Streibel warmed to the idea right away, as Clifford wooed him with flattery.

"We had to have somebody driving this bill," Clifford recalls. "My thought was that we probably had a little more opposition in the Senate. But if we got Bryce in there coordinating the thing, we wouldn't be having a lot of back and forth once the bill got introduced."

There was one other factor Clifford had banked on.

"Bryce had done a lot of things for other people over the years," he said, "and he had a lot of markers out there. I knew he'd call them in and get it done. He was tenacious. He had almost tunnel vision on this."

While Clifford was flying back to Grand Forks, Streibel was at his desk in his den doing some serious thinking. He knew that a lot of legislators and doctors had their own good reasons for opposing an expanded medical school. But he saw the issue in a slightly different light, not just in terms of cost or tertiary care potential.

"I saw the issue as us being able to offer our young people an opportunity to go into the medical profession. I didn't care if even one of them came back and lived in North Dakota. It wasn't an issue of how many would come back and practice in North Dakota, but whether we were going to deny North Dakota kids the chance," he recalls.

With his resolute tunnel vision firmly in place, Streibel began reviewing what needed to be done. Clifford was right: an interim study had to be made, for this was the kind of controversial bill that would never fly coming from a lone member of the legislature. It would never get out of committee.

There was also the problem of the money they needed to appropriate for the new medical school. It would be a big chunk and the governor didn't have it in the budget. But of course, the governor in 1971 might not be the governor in 1973. For Art Link had announced he was giving up his Congressional seat to run for governor. That was a plus. Still, the most pressing issue was the makeup of the interim committee itself. That seemed like the first order of business in overcoming Imperial Cass.

Even before that, however, Streibel needed to check with Em Murray, the executive director of the Legislative Council. It was December 1971, and by now the special interim committees looking into various issues between the 1971 and 1973 sessions were already at work. It was awfully late to be creating another one.

"Em," said Streibel to Murray, "I think I'd like to do this. Can we do it?"

Murray, ever the good soldier, didn't like to say no. But this was a close call.

"I told Bryce we didn't have any budget for another committee. Our limited staff was already on fifty-five-hour weeks."

Streibel expected such an answer. But he waited. He knew Em Murray pretty well.

"So then," said Murray, "I said if it's a committee for consideration of stuff other people will bring in to us and we can evaluate it ... well, I think we could do it."

He based his optimism on the longstanding relationship the Council had established over the years with North Dakota's colleges and universities. Often when his staff did research into an issue, they found themselves calling on various experts within the academic community for help.

He reasoned that since Gary Dunn was already undertaking the same kind of study the Legislative Council would pursue, it didn't make sense to duplicate efforts.

"We'd probably go out and do the same things they were doing," he told Streibel. "They've got professionals doing it and also they're doing it with their dollars, not ours. And, anyway, we don't have the dollars to do it."

Of course, Murray knew that UND's conclusions were going to favor the four-year medical program, but he was confident his staff could sift through any subjective remarks or one-sided information.

"So I told Bryce, let's go ahead with it."

Streibel then asked the key question.

"Who do you think I should appoint chairman?"

Murray grins as he recalls this conversation. "I said, 'I think I know who it would be, but he's already chairing two other committees for you,' Bryce."

"You're thinking of the same guy I am," replied Streibel. "Oscar Solberg."

"Yeah," said Murray. "But I don't think he'll do it."

And he was right. Well, almost.

Because Streibel was a UND graduate, he didn't want to chair the committee himself. Oscar Solberg, on the other hand, wasn't a UND grad, wasn't even a Republican. He was a farmer, semi-retired and more or less the elder statesman of the Legislature. During the years when Democrats controlled the House, he'd been the Speaker and had impressed his colleagues with his low-key confidence. Democrat and Republican alike trusted him and liked him.

"If he told you something, it was a bond," recalls Vern Wagner, a former legislator from Bismarck.

"He was a very nice, taciturn Scandinavian," adds Clifford. "A good, solid thinker, very reliable and honorable. Plus, he was very strong with the governor."

That's true, says Art Link. "Oscar Solberg was a gem. He was a strong Democrat, liberal but highly respected by both parties. Oscar had a modest educational background. He was a farmer out there on the land."

Only recently, Solberg had pulled off a remarkable feat of diplomacy. A fire had destroyed two major buildings at the state industrial school at Ellendale. In deciding whether to rebuild, the Legislature realized that enrollments had fallen off at Ellendale to only 116 students. It just didn't make sense to keep pouring money into it. So they voted to close it down.

But the old school was a central part of small-town Ellendale's life. In looking around for the right emissary to oversee the closing of the school, Streibel faced a dilemma. He knew that the folks in Ellendale were none too happy. He'd heard them voice loud displeasure at the state and state legislators in particular. The man he sent down there to explain everything either had to be a saint or wrapped in a bullet-proof vest.

Actually, no dilemma at all. Oscar Solberg was the ideal man for the job. When Streibel picked him, other legislators breathed a sigh of relief. For in Solberg, the citizens of Ellendale found a consoling voice of reason and empathy.

"For a person to go through that and come out with a clean hide was a monumental achievement," says Art Link. "Oscar had to go to those people and tell them how good it would be for them or why it had to be. The community was distraught to think they'd lose their institution. He made the Legislature proud of him."

But so often in life, the reward for doing well in an impossible situation is that you get called on to do it again. So Streibel took a deep breath and placed another call to the gentleman farmer from Rolla. When he told Oscar what he wanted him to do, he heard only silence on the other end of the line.

Then Oscar said, "Bryce, I thought you were a friend of mine."

After an exchange of half-hearted chuckles, Solberg added, "I'm not a professional in this field."

"You don't need to be a professional," Streibel countered. "We've got all the professionals we need coming in to talk to us. We need good, solid common sense and evaluation."

Finally, reluctantly — as Streibel knew he would — Solberg agreed.

"It was a smart move on his part to appoint Oscar," says Link. "It was a dirty job. Like a big brother telling his little brother, 'You go clean the chicken house.'"

"Oh, he knew how hot it was," adds Streibel with a grin. "But he had that character trait of neutrality."

With his chairman in place, Streibel turned eagerly — and quickly — to the lineup of the rest of the committee. He makes no bones about his thought process.

"I have to admit this," he says today. "I had a bias and I said if I'm going to appoint a committee, I'm going to exert that bias. So anybody who was adamantly opposed to a four-year school didn't get on the committee. I didn't believe in having opponents and supporters on the committee. I was chairman of the Council and this was one of the privileges I had."

Streibel knew that once the Legislature reconvened in 1973, each party caucus would look to its corresponding members on the Interim Committee on Medical Education and Services for guidance on how to vote.

"That became my plan," he says. "I wanted to develop a strong nucleus in each caucus in each house of the legislature. So, no, there was going to be no C. Warner Littens on that committee."

With the help of Earl Strinden, who was always in close contact with fellow Marine Clifford, Streibel picked a committee equally balanced among Republicans and Democrats. Party affiliation didn't matter. Just a solid sense that each member selected was already friendly toward the medical school.

Among their number were Lee Christiansen, a farmer and Democratic leader in the Senate; Evan Lips, the long-time legislator and Bismarck mayor and three-time all-conference football star at UND; Bob Nasset, a conservative Republican rancher, a person who didn't always vote no and a person who could bring in the conservative support; George Unruh, a Republican from Grand Forks; Art Bunker, a well-thought-of NDSU grad from Fargo who later became Speaker of the House; Ralph Dotzenrod, a Democrat and an implement dealer from the small town of Wyndmere who was greatly admired for his business acumen; Robert Peterson, a manager of a medical clinic. Back in Williston when he was the high school basketball coach, one of his players was Phil Jackson, the UND great and famed coach of the Chicago Bulls and Los Angeles Lakers. Peterson later became state auditor.

Finally, there was the almost legendary Bryndhild Haugland, the committee's only woman, yet the person who ended up serving longer in the State Legislature than anyone in North Dakota history. A big, tall, angular woman, Haugland was a tough-minded, Norwegian spinster from Minot. A Republican who was extremely independent and very interested in human services and commanded wide respect. If she liked an idea, the rest of the Minot legislative contingent liked it, too.

Recently, as Clifford recounted that mission to Fessenden in 1971, and the way the committee was selected, he paused in his reminiscence and smiled. "So, now you get a flavor of how we did it," he said. "In many ways the idea was altruistic. But the way we did it was ruthless."

The Battle Is Joined

10

Toward the end of 1971, with the Fessenden cabal in place, Tom Clifford had one more very calculated maneuver to make.

In his talks with Bob Eelkema, he had learned a good deal about the Division of Health Manpower at the National Institutes of Health. He knew about Doug Fenderson, the North Dakota native who was highly placed at NIH and had assisted Eelkema in getting that MEDEX grant. Gary Dunn and Willard Wright had briefed him on the early findings of the study Dunn was preparing. Clifford knew about the large number of patient contacts in North Dakota that might offset the need for a tertiary care hospital. The idea of a community-based medical school was discussed in some detail — medical students working alongside practicing doctors out in the state's communities.

He knew that if the Legislature authorized a four-year medical school, the university would want to be at the head of the line in Washington when federal grants of any kind became available. In fact, Dunn and Wright urged him to apply immediately for funding.

To do that, however, Clifford would need approval from the state's Board of Higher Education. And that posed a problem. First of all, it was contrary to his style. As president of the university, Clifford operated on the John West principle that it was easier to ask forgiveness than to ask for permission. However, doing an end run around the Fargo contingent was one thing; sliding past the Board was going to be even trickier.

By the end of 1971 it was no secret that a movement was afoot to create a four-year medical school. The talk was everywhere. In November 1971, for instance, the state's Health Planning Council had held an interagency forum in Bismarck to kick around all aspects of allied health education in North Dakota. The four-year medical school idea was the main buzz.

Clifford had managed very carefully, however, to make sure none of the buzz came from him, or from the university in any official capacity. As far as the Board was concerned, the Gary Dunn report on the medical school was being funded by the state's Regional Medical Program, headed by Willard Wright, who had no formal connection to the university. Publicly, Clifford remained aloof from the fray, even as he privately helped orchestrate the persuasive arguments by respected medical men such as Wright or powerful politicians like Earl Strinden and Evan Lips. Officially, though, he hadn't said a word about a four-year medical school to the Board, and they hadn't asked him about it, either.

It wasn't that Clifford didn't have good relations with individual members of the Board — they, after all, had hired him only a year earlier. But while they liked him personally, the hot potato political issue of the medical school was an entirely different matter. Clifford knew that individual members of the Board were afraid of the idea. Indeed, Dick Davison, the Board's executive secretary in those years, recalls more than one member groaning aloud to others, "Man, I hope they don't hang a medical school on us." Some of those Board members had higher political aspirations, after all.

They included George Sinner, a West Fargo man who would go on to become governor one day.

For Clifford to tip his hand before he knew he had the right cards would have been disastrous. Had the Board been aware of his plans, it very likely would have rejected the medical school plan before the battle was even engaged. The risk didn't deter him, however. As Davison puts it, with a Nordic grin, "Tom Clifford had many unique ways of accomplishing things, some of them Irish and sneaky. He was an artist at that."

Clifford's ultimate plan was not to approach the Board at all. But if the university was going to get in line for federal funds, the Board had to give its permission to apply. So the game was this: how to get the Board to approve an application for funding a four-year medical school without asking the Board to approve of a four-year medical school idea in the first place.

In December, at its regular meeting, Clifford presented the four-year medical school question to the Board as if it had come spontaneously from various medical people and respected legislators across the state and not him. The argument those people had presented to him, he told the Board — and certainly not his argument — was that any federal monies available could only be applied for by the university. Since only the Board could approve such a grant, he left them to chew on it.

The Board met in a conference room next to Clifford's office, and deliberated all day long and into the evening. In the dark hours, Clifford poked his head into the room. Kenny Raschke, the commissioner of higher education who worked for the Board, posed the question. "Well, what do you think, Tom?"

"I remember it clearly," says Clifford. "I said, 'I don't think we have a choice.' I said, 'I think if we want to have quality health care in North Dakota, and if we want to give North Dakota kids access to being a doctor, we better pull out all the stops and get it done. The Board should at least apply for funding.'"

They looked at each other and nodded their heads.

But Clifford wasn't going to leave the meeting without something official. He wanted something in hand, something in writing. However, it was late and all the secretaries had gone home. Perhaps, had the Board been a little more observant, they might have realized how important the matter was to the president. Because, for of all Clifford's traits and accomplishments, there was one thing everyone seemed to know about him: he abhorred memos. He never wrote them. He never wrote letters. He was a verbal man.

Yet there he was that night, sliding paper into a typewriter and punching out a letter of approval from the Board. It was a rare sight. He rolled the letter out of the machine and made sure Peter Hinrichs, the chairman of the Board, signed it. The next day he asked Eelkema to take the application to Washington. Thus, the first official decision on the new medical school had been made — very likely without the deciders being quite aware of what they'd done.

The letter from the Board of Higher Education now gave Clifford the political flexibility to go public with his official support for the four-year medical program. In fact, he no longer worried about the Board. It was his intention never to formally bring up the topic with them again. Certainly, they weren't about to press the issue either.

In the meantime, the president of the university could show up at the meetings of Oscar Solberg's Interim Committee on Medical Education and put the official Clifford stamp of approval on the idea. Just in case anyone really wondered where he stood.

Solberg wasted no time, gaveling the first meeting of the interim committee to order at 10:10 A.M., in what was then known as the Large Hearing Room in the State Capitol at Bismarck on January 28, 1972.

Among those who filled the room were some of the elite of North Dakota politics and medicine. Along with Streibel and a handful of other legislators, the meeting had attracted the attention of Governor William L. Guy — who would turn over the reigns to fellow Democrat Art Link after the fall election. From UND, Clifford had brought along Harwood, his reluctant dean, and Wally Nelson, John Vennes and Bob Eelkema. Willard Wright also was there, along with Gary Dunn, listed as representing the North Dakota Medical Research Foundation.

Streibel opened the meeting with some clarifying remarks. Candidly, he laid out the three choices, as he saw it: either there would be no medical school in the future or there would be a full-fledged, four-year degree-granting program, or there would be some kind of vague financial arrangement with other states.

He admonished members of the interim committee that they had "perhaps the greatest responsibility of any of the Legislative Council's interim committees, because of the far ranging impact your decisions and recommendations will have on the state and its citizens for years to come."

Presently, Solberg got the meeting under way by introducing Ted Harwood.

It made sense. He was the dean of the School of Medicine, after all, and a good one by almost everyone's assessment.

"He was a remarkable dean," recalls George Magnus Johnson, M.D., one of Harwood's students and still a faculty member at the medical school. "He knew all about every one of his students. That's the way it should be in a small medical school. When you go to a large medical school, the last thing a department chair knows is your name, where you came from, your goals and aspirations. Harwood knew all of that."

He had his quirks, they say, especially a penny-pinching nature that many ascribed to his rearing in Vermont (which, to a non-North Dakotan, seems a lot like the pot calling the kettle black). He seldom approved air travel, insisting everyone ride the train. A true academic, Harwood was known for a favorite saying: "A word to the wise is unnecessary."

Yet he heavily encouraged research in basic sciences. He was dean when the first Ph.D. was granted by the School of Medicine in the 1950s, and he led the way in the late fifties to building a rehabilitation hospital in Grand Forks.

"He was a fine guy," says Clifford. "But he was the dean and he didn't like the four-year idea. He just didn't think we needed it. I think, though, he was ill and he just couldn't bear the thought of going through all of that."

While he wasn't for the idea, Harwood usually tried not to show it.

"In the beginning," says Bill Harlan, "we sort of worked around him and ignored him. That didn't work well with him. He wasn't too keen on that and I think John Vennes prompted him a little bit."

Still, says Eelkema, "He was a little bit of an unguided missile. In all the talks we gave supporting the four-year school, we never let him go out to meetings alone. We always added John or Wally or myself so we could keep the conversation about the medical school in an appropriately directed fashion. We didn't want to give the idea that we could be ever again a two-year school."

That morning in Bismarck, Harwood to some looked desperately old, a man mired in another century. His comments were limited to a broad outline of trends affecting medical education nationwide. Following that, his main role was to introduce John Vennes and Wally Nelson. Harwood, in fact, wouldn't attend many of the coming meetings.

"The strangest feeling I ever had," says Vennes, "was when Clifford asked me to go to the Legislature [later that year] and present the curriculum for the four-year medical school, and my dean was sitting back in Grand Forks."

Like Harwood, Vennes was a man in love with the basic sciences. Not surprisingly, the two men got along well over the years. "John Vennes knew where the bones were buried, and all the administrative structure," says Clifford. "He liked to get everything in a neat line. He was orderly, he covered all the bases. He had a quiet unassuming way. John never got carried away, but he was dedicated.

Probably more dedicated than enthusiastic about the four-year plan. But he did a superb job."

In fact, during those awkward years from 1971 through 1973 when Harwood had no interest in conducting the four-year enterprise, Vennes picked up the baton. "Whenever there was a lapse in leadership, John stepped forward to provide it," Wally Nelson told Bob Eelkema during an interview in the late 1970s. "John was very instrumental in getting that program under way. He carried it through some very rough spots in the road when the leadership at the medical school wasn't as strong as it could have been. He was sort of a second Clifford."

Twenty-five years later, Nelson hadn't changed his mind. "Oh, he was important," he said of Vennes from his retirement home in Virginia. With a laugh he added, "He also made attractive slides."

The slides are a private joke among those who know Vennes. For as stable as he was in organizing the efforts to expand the school, it was his creative penchant for preparing clear and colorful slides full of important financial and medical data that made people literally sit up and take notice at those dry hearings.

At that first meeting in Bismarck, Vennes put on a slide show, demonstrating that UND's medical school curriculum had been modified in recent years to conform to that of the larger schools students had been transferring to. One of the changes the new curriculum dealt with was the realization that some of the large schools had gotten away from teaching a pure basic science curriculum in the first two years. Until recently, transfers from UND found that their counterparts at places like the University of Minnesota had already undergone some clinical training and were ahead of them in the hands-on aspect of medical school. The point, he told the committee, was that whatever other problems the medical school faced, the curriculum was first class.

Speaking of problems, Wally Nelson then recapped the "handwriting on the wall" news about transfer problems. Medical schools that had once gladly accepted UND students were now under such pressure from citizens of their own states that, as of 1975, the old transfer agreements were no longer in force. The statistics that drove home the urgency were nicely laid out in another array of colorful John Vennes slides.

Willard Wright was next, explaining how the Regional Medical Program connected with the state Medical Association, and noting that the North Dakota Medical Research Foundation was an arm of the RMP. He made an interesting comment about the study Gary Dunn was working on. The purpose of the study, he said, wasn't to make a recommendation one way or the other or to suggest decisions, but merely to provide information for others to decide what was best. It would have been interesting to watch Dunn and Eelkema at that point to see if they exchanged knowing glances. In fact, Wright himself seemed to compromise his stance as an objective outsider by warning the committee. "The problems facing medical education in North Dakota," he said, "are not insoluble but they cannot be solved if individual groups jockey for position and offer conflicting policies."

This set the stage for the first official appearance of the hot-wired Gary Dunn. Though his study had begun only four months earlier and wouldn't be completed for another two months, Dunn came across enthusiastically as the world expert on medical education, especially relating to North Dakota. He first zeroed in on the need for more doctors in North Dakota, noting that the state had only half the number of doctors per thousand residents as the national average. He noted that almost 200 of North Dakota's current doctors — about forty per cent — were graduates of UND's two-year medical school. These were doctors who had returned to the state after getting their degrees elsewhere. But those 200 represented only a quarter of all UND medical school graduates from recent years. A four-year medical school, he said, could mean a fifty per cent retention of the graduating class each year.

Showing the brashness Clifford loved, Dunn confronted one of the major arguments against a four-year medical school. He glibly assured the committee that the old model for medical schools had changed from the reliance on the large university type hospital. He didn't say exactly what it had changed to, probably because it hadn't really changed at all in the minds of most of the nation's doctors. But Dunn was setting up a carefully thought out straw man so he could knock it down. To build one of those big university hospitals, he said, would cost $100 million, at least. Just as committee members were looking aghast, he said not to worry. No such expense was going to be necessary to make a four-year medical school work in North Dakota. In fact, they wouldn't have to build anything.

Sensing their relief, Dunn could now give the committee some real costs that seemed almost like bargain prices compared to $100 million. The state, he said, would need to spend $3 million to $5 million a year to operate the four-year school. Considering that the Legislature had already approved a yearly $2.67 million appropriation for the two-year medical school in 1971–73, the added costs were modest. Of that $2.67 million, $1.4 million came from the mill levy, with the Legislature kicking in the extra $1.27 million. The projected costs to the state for 1973–75 with a four-year program would mean the same $1.4 million from the levy and an appropriation from the General Fund of anywhere from $1.6 million to $3.6 million each year.

In the months to come, exactly how much more the expanded school would cost would be hotly debated. While the university's advocates focused on the modest increase for 1973–75, opponents tried to shift the focus to the multi-millions the larger medical school would cost to future generations.

As Solberg called a recess for lunch, Clifford's team felt they had presented a clear case for the four-year school. But after lunch, the committee began hearing the first negative comments from the other side of the issue.

Dr. Frank Cesare, president of the North Dakota Medical Association — and a resident of Fargo — opened the afternoon session, warning, "The physicians of North Dakota as well as the state's citizens and medical students will not tolerate any institution that will fall short of the highest standards."

Cesare seemed skeptical of Gary Dunn's assurance that a high percentage of the state's doctors pledged to take part in the hands-on training of medical students back in their private practices. "We have no assurances they will actually come through and do the work," said Cesare. The doctors he was associated with were doubtful, he said, that the state could or should have a four-year medical school.

In fact, he challenged one of the central arguments in favor of a four-year school — the need for better care. Citizens of the state, he argued, were receiving excellent medical care. Building of a new hospital or clinic to lure more doctors to an area, he said, wouldn't work because the health care needs in smaller communities were too few to retain a physician.

But even if one disagreed with him — and many did — Cesare said, the real question was whether the state could afford the extra $3 million it might cost for the four-year school. If it couldn't, then all the talk was a "waste of time." The state's fiscal capacity, he remarked ominously, would be a key consideration in May at the annual meeting of the Medical Association when the state's doctors voted whether to support the medical school expansion.

This prompted Brynhild Haugland to say what Clifford already knew. "Unless any proposals for a degree-granting institution have the unanimous approval of the North Dakota Medical Association, there is no point in the state trying to establish one."

Another doctor in the audience, Robert Painter of Grand Forks, echoed Cesare's concerns. He, too, had sensed ambivalence among doctors to the four-year idea. He was convinced the state's doctors wouldn't or couldn't carry out the teaching requirements and that the medical school would have to attract other doctors into the state to teach.

With that, some of the air had clearly been taken out of the sails of the proponents. It didn't help matters at all when Harwood tossed in, "It's good to be a little cautious in this matter."

But then Phil Dahl stepped into the fray. A Bismarck physician and a UND med school grad, Dahl brought an interesting political pedigree to the supporters of the proposal — along with a tenacity they would need in coming months in lobbying the halls of the State Legislature.

Dahl's father, a stalwart Republican, had served more terms as lieutenant governor than anyone in state history. Not only was the Dahl name well known, young Phil had grown up with a solid understanding of politics.

Though he chose medicine over politics, it didn't take him long after opening his Bismarck practice as an internist in 1952 to become a familiar figure in the political structure of the North Dakota Medical Association. He'd already served as speaker of the association's House of Delegates and in 1972 was president-elect of the body.

Consequently, Dahl knew most of the state's legislators by name, having served frequently on the liaison committee between the Legislature and the doctors. There was no question that he had the confidence of the decision-makers in the North Dakota Medical Association and there wasn't anyone involved in medicine in North Dakota who had the connections with influential legislators he had. Such contacts didn't happen by accident. He had learned an important lesson from his father: in any endeavor with the Legislature, "You've got to get the power structure on your side or you're dead."

Fortunately for Clifford, Dahl was another of those conservative Republicans who saw the medical school as a wise investment. "I believed in what we were doing," he says, "and I still do."

So it was that Dahl rose to offer a counterpoint to the comments of Dr. Cesare.

Not true, he said, that the state's doctors were opposed to the four-year medical school. Rather, doctors were waiting for the facts still to come from the all-important report of Gary Dunn — officially referred to now as "The Dunn Report." And as to the potential $3 million cost, "The question is not whether the state can afford it, but rather if the state can afford not to establish one."

Following Dahl's impressive performance, Wally Nelson fully regained the initiative when he noted that there was a timely urgency to create a four-year school. Because of cutbacks in federal research projects, federal funds were coming available to train family-care doctors. And that was precisely what the four-year school planned to do: train doctors to treat general family needs, such as pediatrics, obstetrics, general surgery and routine care.

Finally, speaking to the worries of those in Fargo, Nelson said the plan for a four-year school wasn't at all about aggrandizing the campus in Grand Forks. "What is envisioned is a degree-granting medical school encompassing the entire state."

With that, Brynhild Haugland suggested the committee adjourn and not reconvene until the Medical Association decided where it stood. As if the matter couldn't be pressed home enough, Evan Lips repeated it one more time: it was extremely important for the Medical Association to take a strong position.

The Dunn Report

11

With straight faces, Willard Wright and Gary Dunn had promised Oscar Solberg's interim committee that The Dunn Report would be an objective assembling of facts about the School of Medicine at UND, not a list of suggestions or recommendations.

But on March 24, 1972, when Dunn submitted his twenty-six-page report, "North Dakota Health Manpower," to Wright's Medical Research Foundation — whose board also was the board of the North Dakota Medical Association — the cat was more or less out of the bag. For in its pages, Dunn cleverly built a subtle case for the expansion to a four-year school while appearing to consider quite seriously the other options.

For example, the report listed four possible actions the state and university could take to resolve the problem of shrinking numbers of medical school transfers. For three of those possibilities — close the medical school, do nothing, or simply pay other states to take UND transfers — the report named slight advantages, and then went into considerable detail regarding disadvantages.

When the report examined the fourth option — develop a degree-granting medical school — it began with advantages but never did get around to finding a single negative element.

In preparing the report, Dunn (and his faithful sidekick, Bob Eelkema) had met with doctors across the state and visited the Fargo Clinic and Dakota Clinic in Fargo, Quain and Ramstad clinics in Bismarck, and the Grand Forks Clinic. They'd also given talks to district medical societies and various groups of allied health professionals.

By the time Dunn faced the interim committee, much of the data in the first phase of the report had already been released — the hard facts about transfer difficulties, the shortage of doctors in the state, and the maldistribution of physicians, most of whom were clustered around the four large cities of Fargo, Bismarck, Minot and Grand Forks.

Dunn played up the angle that North Dakota kids were smart, but when they applied to medical schools in other states they faced competition weighted in favor of native students.

In 1971, he noted, North Dakota had the highest percentage in the country of applicants accepted into a first-year medical school class. Of the seventy-six who applied, fifty-one were accepted into various medical schools, forty-six at UND.

Dunn cited a recent survey of current UND medical school students, two-thirds of whom said they wouldn't be in medical school if North Dakota didn't have a program. Yet, only one in five planned to return to North Dakota after getting a medical degree elsewhere.

"At the writing of this report," Dunn stated, " UND is receiving a record number of applications for the first sixty-three seats in the fall 1972 class: 450 applications." Of those, 227 were from out-of-state hopefuls. But in fact, the medical school seldom admitted out-of-staters and when it did, it gave priority to states with no medical school at all.

Now, said Dunn, although the fifty-six graduating students at UND in 1971 successfully competed for the 295 third-year slots available in other medical schools around the country, an alarming development threatened their continued success. Of those third-year slots, 108 had been from foreign schools compared to an average of only twenty foreign transfers in the past three years, "thus intensifying competition for these few seats at an astonishing rate."

The competition also was heightened by an extremely low attrition rate in the nation's medical schools — only one per cent had dropped out in the past year.

Dunn noted that the state had contributed a little more than half of the School of Medicine's 1971 budget. While the federal government had kicked in forty per cent, almost all of that was earmarked for research projects. The medical school, after all, included more than future doctors. It encompassed 769 total students, enrolling besides medical students, undergraduate and graduate students in physical therapy, occupational therapy, medical technology, cytotechnology, the bio-medical sciences and nursing.

Dunn dropped in a subtle reminder to readers that North Dakotans had, for years, been getting their medical school at dirt cheap prices. In 1969, for example, North Dakota's medical school budget was the lowest in the country — and the next three lowest spent between $3.5 and $5 million annually. Nationwide, the median expenditure was $14.5 million.

Another subtle hint: the UND medical school got only $129,000 in grants from foundations the previous year. "The smaller the medical school, the less competitive it is for other than state monies," wrote Dunn. This was especially true of two-year schools. And it could be worse. Dunn noted that whereas North Dakota provided fifty-two percent of its medical school's expenses, South Dakota ponied up more than three-quarters of the bill for its medical school.

As to the debate that doctors wouldn't be willing to teach in a four-year medical school, Dunn cited a survey that showed nine out of ten physicians were very interested. In fact, most of those who weren't cited pending retirement.

And what of the "Big University Hospital" question? The Dunn Report hammered this once-supposed necessity into little pieces.

"The commonly quoted standard of the number of hospital beds required for teaching is ten beds per student per entering class," he noted. "A medical school with fifty students would require a 500-bed hospital. In actual fact, of schools recently building university hospitals, the range of beds per student is 2.7 to 6.3 or an average of 4.5."

In contrast, he listed the 1,836 total patient beds available in the nine hospitals found in Minot, Grand Forks, Fargo and Bismarck.

"We are comfortable," he said, "with the fact that adequate patient material does exist should the medical community provide access to their patients and should the medical school develop a plan to take advantage of it."

With that very objective warm-up out of the way, Dunn got to the peanut of his study: Alternatives for Action.

One: Cease Operation of Medical School
After all, many short-sighted opponents had asked why not just close the medical school and save a lot of money?

If so, said Dunn, the only advantage was a short-term financial gain to the state. But that gain could easily be offset, he warned, if the state decided to start another medical school in the future.

The disadvantages to option one were many.

That high rate of acceptance of North Dakota students into medical schools would drop like a stone. Currently, the first-year class at UND numbered fifty-three students, or 8.6 per 100,000 population. Of the states without medical schools, the number of their residents in medical schools was significantly lower. He cited the following: Alaska 1.7; Delaware 5.1; Idaho 3.2; Maine 1.9; Montana 3.7; Nevada 2.9, and Wyoming 5.2.

Close the school, and the number of North Dakota students who could hope to become doctors would be almost too small to measure.

Another drawback of closure: over the years, the medical school had become a basic industry in the state. Without it, job opportunities likely would dry up and federal dollars would stop flowing. For every dollar North Dakota currently spent on medical education, Dunn wrote, the state got ninety-two cents in federal contracts.

One more negative: without a medical school, the prestigious science program at UND would suffer. Dunn estimated that as many as twenty-five science faculty would look elsewhere for work.

Two: Contractual Relationship with Degree Granting Schools
Dunn considered two scenarios here. The first involved the state paying other states a per-capita fee for transferring third-year students to their medical schools. The second looked at the idea of paying other states a per-capita rate for the entire four years.

The sole advantage listed: by paying and contracting for a certain number of years, UND students would be guaranteed transfer slots.

Again, the negatives were severe.

"North Dakota would be 'renting' rather than 'buying,'" wrote Dunn, "and would see less medical care return for dollars invested."

The medical school would lose federal funds since recent legislation favored degree-granting schools.

Even with a per-capita fee paid to other states — as low as $5,000 at Nebraska and as high as $30,000 at Michigan, in one estimate — it still might be difficult to find schools with available slots. The added problem here was that many of these schools might be located in distant regions, making it more unlikely that graduating doctors would come back to North Dakota.

The idea of hiring another state to provide all four years of medical school education was new and seemed improbable to Dunn. He cited thorny jurisdictional questions that needed to be ironed out and the likelihood of protracted political squabbles. He said he had even explored the idea with Minnesota and South

Dakota of combining resources with North Dakota to build a regional medical school, but found no positive response.

Three: Maintain Status Quo

In spite of the dire predictions about the future of two-year schools, there were many in the state who didn't believe them and thought things should remain as they were.

The advantage to that, said Dunn was "little turmoil or interference."

The disadvantage: The state had an opportunity now to apply for federal funding designed to help two-year schools expand. The 1971 Comprehensive Health Training Act called for such funds. Programs were being developed to award $50,000 a student from a two-year school who was enrolled in an expanded third-year class. These were some of the funds Clifford had in mind when he got the Board of Higher Education to grant permission to start an application. The deadline, though, was fast approaching. If the state delayed, it would be too late to get third and fourth-year programs in place to get those funds.

There were also, he noted, other capitation grants from the Bureau of Health Manpower Education at NIH of $2,500 a student in the first, second and third years of expanded medical schools.

Four: Develop a Degree Granting Medical School in North Dakota

Though listed "objectively" as just one of four options, the space and enthusiasm devoted to the expansion option, especially saving it for last, made it seem, well, almost like a recommendation.

No negatives were listed.

The key advantage: an almost certain increase in the number of doctors in the state. Of course, the high rate of acceptance of North Dakota students into medical schools would remain high and the transfer problem would evaporate. Meanwhile, the economy would benefit through the addition of more federal monies.

Dunn then listed a prioritized list of steps that would have to be taken to make a four-year program happen. Ironically, the first item on the list was authorization from the Board of Higher Education. Going to the Board for a formal okay was something Clifford was not about to do. But to leave its approval off such a list would be a slap in the face to Board members. Inclusion at the head of the list was, in fact, politically correct.

Other musts on the laundry list:

- The State Legislature had to approve funding
- The university had to make use of existing facilities
- The American Association of Medical Colleges had to bestow accreditation of the four-year program
- Federal funding had to be available
- The clinical staff of the medical school would need release-time from administrative duties to practice medicine
- No limited specialty fields would be part of the curriculum
- With proper supervision, community hospitals and practicing doctors would provide instruction
- Postdoctoral training in the form of residencies must be available
- The majority of clinical training would take place in Grand Forks, Fargo, Bismarck and Minot

In his conclusion, Dunn noted — echoing the words of Brynhild Haugland and Evan Lips — "The future of the medical school will be decided by the physicians of the state at the annual convention in May."

It was clear, he said, that doctors must not only like the idea, they had to be willing to teach, to grant access to their facilities, and to let students work on their patients.

Big Night in Minot

12

In spite of the optimism of Phil Dahl, Gary Dunn and Willard Wright about the willingness of the state's doctors to go along with the four-year medical school, there was, in fact, more ambivalence and outright skepticism in the medical profession than they wanted to admit. A positive vote at the May meeting of the Medical Association was no sure thing.

Much of the doubt was said to be over the issue of quality. Doctors didn't want to see a half-baked medical school turning out incompetent doctors. That high-minded ideal was supposed to be their main bone of contention. "A lot of these doctors," says Vern Wagner, "came through training in the big county hospitals, like the Cook County Hospital in Chicago, where the huge patient load was mostly charity cases." Wagner, the executive director of the North Dakota Medical Association at the time, was also a member of the House of Representatives from Bismarck. "This was before Medicare. Well, we didn't have any hospitals like that in North Dakota, and that seemed to be the biggest concern."

But there was another explanation for the hesitancy of some doctors, much less publicized but no less real.

Part of it had been hinted at in the first meeting of the interim committee. More than a few doctors, especially ones in Fargo, thought a four-year school would never fly in North Dakota unless outside doctors were brought in to do the teaching. This conclusion reflected their own big city experience, as Wagner says. Teaching was supposed to be done by professional faculty who had been trained in specific medical specialties, and not by everyday general practitioner doctors. Their concern, however, wasn't so much that bringing in these specialists from outside would cost the state money — which it would, if that's what happened.

The primary concern of those doctors was the money it would cost them, personally. They just couldn't help seeing the medical school as unwanted competition and a threat to their income.

"They were very concerned that faculty would be brought in and the faculty would be out there competing with them for patients," says Bill Harlan. "That didn't sit very well."

"No question," agrees Grandon Tolstedt, a Bismarck surgeon and a solid supporter of the medical school plan. "They were afraid of competition."

Yet even within the competition issue, loss of income wasn't the only fear.

"They thought there would be a large number of faculty recruited from the outside and that they themselves would become second-class citizens," says Harlan. "If I come in as a specialist and you're a general practitioner in a small community, people will start to gravitate to me because I'm a specialist. And as you get more and more specialists, people will shop around and go to the gastroenterologist and not the GP. They were concerned that the university system would create more specialists and they would be marginalized more and more."

Of course, the Dunn Report had said the training would be done by in-state doctors and that the four-year medical school wouldn't create post-graduate residencies in limited specialty areas. Everything was aimed at producing doctors who could care for as wide a spectrum of patients as possible.

But as the Medical Association convened at the Ramada Inn in Minot that May, it became clear, says Wagner, that those who supported the idea of a degree-granting medical school thought the Dunn Report was very good and those who did not support it, didn't really believe it.

Of course, the May meeting wasn't the first time the state's doctors had discussed the idea of a medical school expansion. Ever since Dunn in his ill-fitting suit had been given the go-ahead a year earlier to develop his study, the various district councils of the Medical Association had been the scenes of long and often contentious debate. And none of the fervor from those earlier meetings had been left behind when the Minot meeting was gaveled to order.

The Medical Association operates on a committee system and the issue of the medical school had been referred to the committee on education. There wasn't much drama about how that committee would vote, so its measure of support for the expansion went immediately to the reference committee. That's where most of the action took place. The committee began taking testimony from any doctors who wanted to speak and so many signed up that two days were required to hear them all. Ultimately, the reference committee voted to send the medical school measure to its full House of Delegates for final consideration.

The testimony in the reference committee was divided essentially between doctors from the more rural areas, who strongly supported the expanded school, and doctors from the bigger cities, who were more apprehensive.

"But it was a good debate," says Wagner. "A very good debate. Those that opposed it were very sincere in their opposition. Sometimes it's hard to change people's minds. Most of the people who went to big schools in big cities couldn't fathom the idea that you could replicate that training in a smaller setting."

That myth was refuted by doctors such as Dean Strinden, the brother of the assistant House floor leader, Earl Strinden. Dean had practiced medicine in Williston since 1954 when he got his medical degree and post-graduate training at the University of Colorado. He'd done his basic science training at the two-year school in Grand Forks.

In the mid-1950s an oil boom had caused a chain-reaction population explosion in Williston. It suddenly needed doctors, and Strinden and two college friends opened their own practice. One of the men he eventually worked with was Willard Wright.

Strinden became active in medical society affairs and served in the House of Delegates and as president of the association. Since his clinical training had come at one of those big city hospitals, he had the standing to say what he did.

"Most of the illnesses of humankind," he says, "are not found in the big hospitals. Yes, the more sophisticated problems that require sophisticated treatment are in the big hospital centers. But the usual, everyday maladies and illness, you don't see those."

It's the general practitioner, the family practice doctor, in North Dakota, who sees the most common cases that affect people, he argued.

"We had a totally different concept from that of any other medical school in the country," he recalls. "The concept was to farm the students out to other communities and other doctors to get the types of training that they needed."

What about teaching?

"I think a lot of men thought it was their duty to teach," says former Bismarck surgeon Grandon Tolstedt. "I felt that way. Teaching is interesting because it makes you keep up to date. Makes you study. Some youngster comes along and asks a stupid question. But is it really stupid? You've got to go find out."

122

"No," adds Bismarck physician Phil Dahl, "there was never a problem getting physicians to teach. Physicians were anxious to help."

Among the doctors rising to defend the idea of a degree-granting medical school were Larson from Velva, McClain from Hillsboro and Wolf from Dickinson. Wally Nelson appeared and in his abrupt cowboy fashion told his colleagues to "get off your duffs. We're losing our transfer students."

But the medical politicians in Fargo, led by senior doctors from the area, took the argument in the other direction. It became clear that this was not going to be a unanimous vote.

"We were in a bind," says Dahl. "I felt about it as an emergency. We would never get the Legislature without physician support."

The night before the vote by the full House of Delegates, clusters of supporters and opponents gathered in rooms at the Ramada Inn. The outcome was not so much in doubt as the unanimity of the vote. A split vote would be almost as bad as a defeat.

What the supporters needed at the moment was an elder statesman, someone who could go into those rooms and appeal to his colleagues on a rational and professional level. What they needed was, well, Moses.

"Willard was the guy, after all, who said if we don't have the doctors' backing we can kiss it goodbye," says Bob Eelkema.

Willard Wright had told friends frequently over the years that he wanted to do something for the medical school. "Perhaps I inherited a little something from my father," he once explained to Eelkema.

Wright's father, a Scottish immigrant, was a teacher married to the daughter of a prominent Manitoba politician. Thomas Greenwave later became premier of the province. The career of Wright's father rose along with that of his father-in-law. He served on several provincial advisory boards aimed at developing educational programs.

As a doctor, Willard Wright was known not only as a skilled diagnostician but as an efficient administrator. Early in his career he'd served on the Williston school board and helped develop the junior college there into the University of North Dakota at Williston. Before his involvement in the governance of the AMA he had served on North Dakota's Board of Medical Examiners and even served a term as president of the state Medical Association.

When he became head of the Regional Medical Program he started building educational programs around the needs of rural doctors. It's why he liked Eelkema's MEDEX program so much.

"The people in North Dakota have always been appreciative of good quality medical care," he told Eelkema. "They feel very deeply about this and they recognize they have to pay for it. It's why they voted the one-mill levy in 1948. It just seemed to me that we, the doctors, had an obligation to repay the people by providing more educational opportunities and better chances for them to get good care."

The best way to do that, he believed, was to improve the medical school.

That night in Minot, word began circulating that a group of doctors was preparing a minority report stating profound opposition to the expansion of the medical school. It was to be submitted by the reference committee to the House of Delegates the next day along with its recommendation that the issue come to a full membership vote. It was a fire that had to be put out if the cause was to survive.

Wright, a master of the diplomatic art of maneuvering disparate groups to consensus, went to work. He later recounted for Eelkema in detail his approach that night.

"Basically, there was an anti-group from Fargo who had apparently been instructed to oppose the resolution. When you have a big thing going before the House of Delegates you never know for sure where you stand. You go to the reference committee and make your pitch. Of course, as the night wears on, the reference committee is writing their report and recommendation. It just happens that you may drift around all night and discuss it with the various members. Perhaps clarify a point. While you are clarifying the point you can discuss it with them."

As it turned out, gentle point-clarifying from Moses was like arm-twisting from Samson. By morning, the Fargo opposition hadn't been dissuaded from its opposition, but Wright had succeeded in quashing the minority report and in winning a positive recommendation from the reference committee.

When the House of Delegates voted that morning, some grumbling could still be heard. But the vote carried by a substantial majority — though it was not unanimous. If it was not a complete strategic coup it was an important tactical victory. The vote gave the university the legitimacy to move forward according to the Dunn Report's guidelines. It committed doctors to teaching and allowing the medical school access to their patients and facilities.

Oddly, Wright told friends afterwards, the extent to which most doctors did approve of the expansion concept could be credited in great part to a most unlikely source: Dean Ted Harwood. For it was Harwood who had created a summer program some years back that dispersed UND medical students to the offices of practicing physicians in the state. Known as the MECO program and organized with the aid of medical student George Blatti, it was a month-long visit during the summer, where students mostly observed real physicians performing their everyday duties. But it had an effect no one had counted on. A positive bond had been established during those many summers between the medical school and practicing doctors who hadn't graduated from there. In essence, a hidden network of support existed all along that few people knew anything about.

The Chuck House Gang

13

The approval of the Medical Association was like the starter's pistol going off at a track meet. The rest of the summer was a blur of action for the small coterie of medical school supporters within the university.

One of the first to move was Tom Clifford. He immediately flew to Chicago to cover a very important base. Even if the Legislature went on to approve the plan, the four-year medical school was going to have to win accreditation from the American Association of Medical Colleges.

"Mr. Clifford," said the man at AAMC in Chicago, "I don't think it's possible. You don't have a big hospital out there."

The sound of those same old words had become such a tiresome drone. It was frustrating. Couldn't naysayers come up with something more original?

"You only have 50,000 people in Grand Forks," said the man from AAMC. "Medical students would never have enough unusual cases to work on. Blah, blah and blah."

Clifford fell back on Irish humor.

"Yeah," he said, "but I've had most of those diseases they'll be talking about. They can work on me."

This won him a chuckle but not much more.

"He was a very nice guy," Clifford recalls, "but I could see him thinking, 'That poor dumb bastard ... .' He said, 'Good luck.' I said, 'We're gonna take a run at it, that okay with you?' He said, 'Well, yeah, we won't stand in your way but after three years you're going to have to have the approval.'"

"We'll make the cut," Clifford assured him, though he wasn't at all sure himself.

"I didn't know how we'd do it, but I couldn't tell him I didn't know if we could or not. I admit it. It was awesome. And I knew we'd never have a huge hospital."

He thought about it on the long plane ride back to North Dakota. But rather than feeling defeated, he stepped off the plane invigorated.

"I got hold of the guys. Vennes. Wally Nelson and Bobby. And we formed a cabinet. I put Bobby in charge. Once a week we met at a corner table at the Chuck House of the Westward Ho for breakfast. And we'd plan. We'd sit around the table and have coffee and we'd plan."

Though the old Westward Ho motel on Gateway Drive has recently reopened, the wind-blown Chuck House hasn't seen a customer in years. It still sits there, worn and faded. A passerby would never guess that the some of the most important steps that led to the development of the university's nationally-recognized School of Medicine took place behind its withered planks.

The Chuck House Cabinet had a more formal name: The Medical Advisory Committee, or MAC. It was the brain trust of the whole cabal. It was also pure Clifford. If he didn't like writing memos, he liked formal meetings even less. For one thing, they gave too many people a chance to sink a program.

Which is why he wasn't going to go to the Board of Higher Education for permission. Nor would he ask the Faculty Council at UND what it thought.

"Hell no," he says. "The faculty would never have approved it. They saw the medical school as devouring what limited resources we had. That's why we have today a separate entity for the medical school. It is budgeted separately. That's a key fact. The faculty has their money and the medical school has theirs. That was my idea. I'm Irish enough to do that. You've really got to divide and conquer, so I just said the hell with the Faculty Council."

His approach to committees was similar. "If you appoint an official committee, you immediately separate people from the stream. Everybody assumes things. Some look at the committee and say, 'Well, those guys don't know anything.' So we got together at the Chuck House and had our plan, and everybody was responsible for it. And I'd call them back each week and we'd go around the table and everybody would recite. If they hadn't done something, they had to say why they didn't. It wasn't a bad way to do it. We couldn't bring the dean in because he was against it. So we went with mavericks.

"And they were the right people at the right time — a critical time — doing the right thing. The stars were all lined up. I'm not good at that — organizing something around a process. I'm a contrarian. I know myself, and there're a lot of things I can't do that they did. There was no way I could sell the doctors. I didn't have the inventiveness that Bobby had. Or the organization that Vennes had. I could never have done that."

As Clifford saw it, his role in the campaign was to expedite things.

"My function was to see that the process went along. I had to plan where we should go next and what we should do and then talk it over with the guys and smooth their paths. I trusted them. I can't think of a single instance where we second-guessed anybody. All these people worked very hard. And scores of others contributed in many ways. But let me tell you, that Chuck House Gang, that's the hard core of it there."

That summer, the Chuck House Gang spread out across the state drumming up new support and cementing old. They spoke before hospital associations, district medical society meetings, and every service club that would have them. They met with legislators, doctors, businesspeople, heads of chambers of commerce. Some of those sessions were less formal than others.

"John and Wally and I would go out and meet with various legislators," recalls Eelkema. "We'd go to dinner and talk about the medical school. But, you know, most people in the Legislature in North Dakota are not well versed in finances. They were everyday farm people. A lot were dairy farmers. Wally was from Nebraska. He wore cowboy boots and a cowboy hat. I'd been a veterinarian. So our discussions were mainly, 'Well, how's the milk production?' What we were doing was saying to them, 'We're part of you, we're part of the state.' That was critical."

In the meantime, thanks to Gary Dunn, the university also had a bona fide outside medical expert to go along on those meetings and lend credibility. He was Bill Harlan, the associate dean in Alabama whom Dunn had persuaded to come to North Dakota to help.

"I went up there as a hired academic gun," Harlan recalls. With his impressive academic resume, and his background as a cardiologist, he was the kind of person doctors would believe if he said the new medical school plan would work. They wouldn't believe Gary Dunn because — among other reasons — he wasn't a physician. Bob Eelkema was a doctor, but he was too local. And of the faculty at the two-year school, even those with M.D. degrees generally were not practitioners.

Harlan came up from Alabama and stayed for a week or two at a time, traveling around with Dunn and Eelkema to various places to answer doctors' questions. He had one other critical assignment. It was his job to invent a way to implement the plan. For while the Chuck House Gang was pressing hard for the big-picture item of creating a four-year school, there were hundreds of little details about how that picture would be hung that hadn't yet been addressed. For instance, if UND was going to send medical students to Minot to train, they'd need a place to live. Where? They'd need a certain core faculty in each city. Who were they? Who was going to officially hire them? They needed, even, very mundane things like a system for communicating grades back and forth to the main campus.

Even so, Harlan recalls, his first take on the situation in North Dakota was positive.

"My first appraisal: 'This is incredible. I thought, if these people can find the money, they can do it.' I looked at the record of the two-year students and how they had done. They included a couple of people I had worked with before. One was Dick Egdahl, the famous transplant surgeon at Massachusetts General. I'd worked with him at the Medical College of Virginia when I ran a transplant unit. He was a two-year UND student who went to Harvard. I began to look at where UND students were being placed. And it was clear they were going to top institutions and doing quite well."

He was impressed by one other item — something, he says, he'll never forget.

"It's a characteristic of the people in North Dakota. When they make up their mind to do something — and if they tell you yes, they're going to do it — by God, they're going to do it. The reverse is also true. If they say no, then you can forget it. I never heard anyone there say probably. It was either yes or no. When I found people who were doubting, they wanted to hear the facts. They had good questions and they listened. Then they didn't blow you off by saying, well, I'll think about it. They took in the information and said, we're gonna do it."

Before very long, he says, "I knew it was going to work. Because it seemed to have the political backing; and there was no question in my mind about the academic credentials — of even the students coming in; the state school system prepared its students well. And the university had a strong core of faculty doing the basic science training. It just seemed to me a sort of slam dunk. It was the right time, the right cast of characters, and the fire underneath it all was Peter Pan, the leprechaun."

Speaking of Gary Dunn, he and Harlan developed a dog and pony show at each talk they gave that summer. Dunn would start things off with what amounted to a frenzied pep talk that laid out a grand vision of what might be. Almost always he skipped over crucial details and concentrated on the broad sweep of his brush. He'd usually end with a Knute Rockne-style motivational speech, exhorting people to look at the positive side and think about how the plan could work and how each and every one of them could make it work.

"He came across as a very rough-hewn person," Harlan recalls. "Gary actually had a bit of the dockworker about him. I think that he could identify with people very well. He liked them and they knew it. His point was always, 'You should believe. Because if you do, you can and you will.'"

At that point in their typical talk, Harlan would step to the podium and mildly chide Dunn for glossing over the nuts and bolts. Harlan knew how he himself came across — as a conservative scientist very much concerned about details.

"Then I would take issue with Gary and what he'd said in a kind of mock way — a good cop/bad cop kind of thing. And we'd disagree on some things. When he needed a detail, I'd provide the detail. But he was always the good cop and I was the doubting person who would bring him — and the plan — back down to reality."

It was a role Harlan warmed to, though when he was first asked to come to North Dakota, he tried to beg off.

"I said, 'Gary, I don't think there's a chance in the world that I could be helpful to these people.' But Gary helped me find a way of looking at things in my psyche that I would have never found. As time went along, I began to see what he did for me and for my approach. As a scientist — I'd been in biochemistry at Duke and been doing clinical trials — I'm the sort of person who starts with a null hypothesis. I neither believe nor disbelieve, but I'm willing to test and to prove. And so I try not to start with a bias. In most of my work, details are everything. Suddenly, I was being asked to do something where normally details were important ... but I watched Gary work and I thought, 'Gee, sometimes the details aren't everything. Sometimes they come along after the concept, the generation of the energy.'

"And that's because he was a kind of leprechaun. He lived in a sort of magical world that in reality doesn't exist. In Gary's world, none of us ever really knew what was true. He was given to broad generalizations. They might be wrong but he could convince you that they were right. And the charge to you was 'implement them.' Well, I'm a problem solver. That appealed to me. He brought out that part of me, that positive 'find a way' attitude. I think he did that with Bob as well. Bob's view, I think, had been very internal North Dakota. Suddenly, Gary made Bob see a totally different, much larger world.

And yet, he adds, "I don't think Gary was honest all of the time. I think he sometimes replaced facts with hyperbole. He was very glib and that always bothers people. I think Harwood was very suspicious of him right from the start. He and Gary were always at odds. I think people began to pick up on his glibness and want documentation of his background. Some became very skeptical of him. People who took the trouble to look and make a few phone calls said, 'I just can't believe anything that person says.'

"I didn't see through Gary right away. Anyplace we ever went, I never had any more fun than I had with Gary. I don't know whether he was really manic-depressive and I was just seeing the manic phase. Gary seemingly had an uninhibited approach to having fun and could get people to release inhibitions.

"So I soon realized how extraordinarily valuable Gary could be. I think he was the right person there at the right time. It seemed the situation was ripe, the politics, the economics, the ability of the students and school. It just took that sort of fire to crystallize it and push it."

So impressed was Harlan that when the VA later asked him to help set up a medical school in eastern Tennessee, he hired Gary to consult with him. "I really valued Gary's ability to look beyond the small temporary kind of barriers and say we can leap those with ease. Let's just keep going. The idea is out there. Let's get on with it."

Over the summer, as more and more doctors began to come aboard, Harlan says he was at first curious why they would change their minds from skeptic to believer.

"I learned something I wouldn't have guessed but should have," he says. "Characteristically, an outside doctor would go to North Dakota and say, 'Look, you've got the fourth lowest ratio of physicians to population of any place in the country.' To which the doctors might say, 'Yeah, but look at our infant mortality rate' — which was then used across the country as the measure of medical care within a state. North Dakota had the second lowest infant mortality in the country.

"So the question was, 'Well, why do we need more physicians if by the one national measure we have we're doing fine?' It was one of the questions that came up among the doctors and among the more knowledgeable specialists and legislative people. It was a question for which I didn't have a good answer.

"Suddenly, it came to Gary Dunn before it came to me, that really what many of the doctors and legislators were talking about wasn't so much more doctors for the state, or better medical care. What they really wanted were educational opportunities for their kids. That really made a difference. They could see the medical school having to decrease enrollments or even, gradually, not existing. And that was something they didn't want. They wanted their young people to have that opportunity. I can tell you that one of the things that takes people out of the state is an educational opportunity that can only be found elsewhere."

The Boys from Raleigh

14

At the start of the summer of 1972, Bob Eelkema had a reputation as the man who knew his way around federal grants — based largely on his success with his MEDEX program. After the North Dakota Medical Association meeting in Minot, Eelkema made a quick trip to Washington to renew contacts with his MEDEX contract officer, Doug Fenderson, the man with the North Dakota connection

Born in Streeter, Fenderson's father had been a railroad engineer who moved the family to St. Paul when Doug was a child. In the late 1960s, young Fenderson had been involved in developing programs for so-called mid-level health workers — nurse practitioners and technicians in physical and occupational therapy — in Minnesota. He'd written an impressive national study for a group called the Commission on Education, for which he'd interviewed the deans of medical schools and attended the meetings of curriculum committees.

The report came to the attention of Paul Sanazaro, who lured Fenderson to Washington to become chief of health manpower research in the brand-new National Center of Health Service

Research. It seemed an ideal fit. The center was studying ways to increase available health care across the country. Fenderson immediately began looking into how to increase the number of doctors.

"There was a serious shortage," he recalls. "You heard lots of jokes about the well-named waiting room."

Several studies had documented the geographic maldistribution of doctors, a situation intensifying as older general practitioners retired and passed from the scene. The MEDEX program to train returning military corpsmen as physician assistants came out of these studies. It's what brought Eelkema to Washington in 1969 where he met Fenderson and won his large grant for a UND program.

In the meantime, by May 1972, the Health Manpower Act had been implemented. Its purpose was to augment or take over some of the results of the demonstration projects that had been started through Fenderson's national center. The federal Bureau of Health Manpower was formed in the NIH, headed by Kenneth Endicott. He was a former director of the National Cancer Institute at the NIH. Endicott heard about Fenderson and asked him to come to NIH to head up the Office of Special Programs. The office had two objectives: first, to implement strategies for the training of mid-level medical workers and physician assistants. In other words, to make official those demonstration programs like Eelkema's that had been funded earlier.

It was familiar ground for Fenderson. But the second half of the bureau's mission was new: to develop the novel concept of Area Health Education Centers or AHEC.

The concept of AHEC had already riled up lots of other health agencies. At the center of the storm was the famous and influential Houston heart surgeon Michael DeBakey — named by Lyndon Johnson in 1967 to head a commission on heart, cancer and stroke. DeBakey had been pushing his concept of centers of excellence — the very plan viewed so skeptically by Willard Wright and the American Medical Association as concentrating too much power in the hands of very few doctors. DeBakey saw the fledgling AHEC concept as a perfect funding mechanism to implement his centers of excellence plan. Again, these centers were supposed to be aligned with large university hospitals and would act as the ultimate clearinghouse for the most serious and difficult cases. The first was to be built in Houston, according to DeBakey's plan.

But because of the opposition of many other influential medical people, "there was a kind of an elephant fight about who would implement that strategy," says Fenderson. DeBakey's group lost the fight and the Bureau of Health Manpower was designated as the developers of the AHEC idea. The bureau's philosophy now was to provide funding for educational programs less grandiose in concept and tailored more to the glaring deficiencies of health care in a given area.

Coincidentally, Fenderson had been brought to the Bureau of Health Manpower at about the time the Dunn Report was circulating among North Dakota doctors. Not long after the North Dakota Medical Association had thrown its support behind the expansion of the medical school, Eelkema found himself in Washington, chatting with Fenderson.

In a fortuitous exchange of ideas, Eelkema told Fenderson about the push in North Dakota to create a four-year medical school. Eelkema explained that they were being opposed by people who kept telling them it couldn't work because they didn't have the big university hospital, or enough concentrated population to provide the required case material.

"But what we do have," said Eelkema, "is a lot of smaller communities with doctors willing to help teach. I think we could make them into a network of training sites."

Fenderson thought immediately that North Dakota could be just the kind of program the bureau was looking for to get its AHEC idea implemented. In essence, he said, AHEC-funded centers in various cities across the state would become the teaching hospitals.

The original AHEC concept envisioned that a state might propose one or two locations for educational centers. "But in North Dakota, the whole state was to be the AHEC," says Fenderson. "I thought it was a neat idea. It was one way of seeing that health workers received first-hand clinical experience in places which had significant medical shortages."

While he offered lots of encouragement — along with application forms — Fenderson was not the person who would ultimately decide which programs would be funded. If their proposal passed muster, he told Eelkema, the bureau would send out a team of inspectors to review the details.

In the meantime, the deadline for applications was only weeks away.

But Eelkema knew exactly what he had to do in those few weeks, because Fenderson had made some specific suggestions. Go back and get the big cities in North Dakota represented, he had said. In each city find a hospital administrator, a legislator, a nurse, a doctor, and elect a chairman. "The whole idea is to maximize the use of your community facilities," said Fenderson.

Eelkema came back to North Dakota wired top to bottom. He and Gary Dunn went immediately to the North Dakota Medical Association where Dunn had no trouble whipping up excitement over the possibility of not only attracting big federal dollars, but finally having a blueprint for framing out this most unusual medical school. When Clifford heard about it at a Chuck House breakfast, he gave his official approval. It was now mid-May and the deadline for the application was mid-June. There was an enormous amount of organizing and writing to be done.

Eelkema and Dunn rushed off to Bismarck, Fargo, Minot and back to Grand Forks, quickly organizing AHEC advisory committees made up of the requisite types Fenderson had suggested. Eelkema asked each committee to appoint a chairman who would then find other leaders in the area to help plan the major and minor details of a potential AHEC clinical center. Grandon Tolstedt was elected chairman of the AHEC organizing committee in Bismarck, Dick Larsen in Minot, John Magnus in Fargo, and William Krech in Grand Forks.

Back in Grand Forks, Dunn took on the writing duties. First, he prepared a generous and glowing letter of support to be signed by each AHEC chairman and used as evidence in the application that the required structure and cooperation was in place.

Dunn then began writing, essentially, the entire grant application, assisted by Eelkema and Nancy Hepburn — soon to be Nancy Dunn. The plan called for a $1.2 million budget in the first year that would cover the costs of deans and assistant deans at each of the four AHECS, a chairman of medicine, a chairman of pediatrics, a chairman of OB/GYN, a chairman of family practice, and so forth, plus monies for rental of clinical space, support services for secretaries and travel money.

"AHEC was an extraordinary opportunity," says Bill Harlan. "The question came up constantly — where are you gonna train these people? The view of medical education and training was quite different in those days. Every place that I had been, the medical school hospital was a cash cow for the university. The University of Michigan made $1 billion or more a year from its university hospital. At the University of Alabama, it was the same thing. Duke, very clearly. But here, in North Dakota, you were talking about a situation that wouldn't be a cash cow. You wouldn't be generating the money to support the medical school so you had to have some way of supporting the clinical training out in these hospitals. And AHEC provided that. It would allow those doctors interested in teaching to come together and teach."

Getting that application together and out on time was a feat.

"Bob was a genius," says Jim Brosseau, a respected Grand Forks internist and Chair of UND's Department of Community Medicine. He's also from Drayton, Eelkema's North Dakota hometown.

"Probably no one is more deserving of credit for our going to a four-year school than Bob. Bob would probably cite himself for that, too."

Brosseau grins as he says this. For Eelkema, no shrinking violet, was a perfect example of what Clifford called his "mavericks."

"Bob was the guy who knew how to persuade people," says Brosseau. "He was kind of a masterful guy in getting things done. And being a maverick, he kept everybody a little bit off balance."

Of course, some people didn't like being off balance.

"We saw a lot of Bob," says Vern Wagner, the executive director of the North Dakota Medical Association then and a Bismarck legislator. "He was around quite a bit. But, I have to say that many of our physicians were not too convinced he was the guy. He was not a practicing physician. He was a public health physician. His philosophy was not quite in line with many of the physicians. They liked John Vennes better. A lot of the guys were in school when John Vennes taught. They took classes from him. Bob Eelkema taught there, too. But he was always dependent on grants. He was just a different kind of person."

Eelkema is very aware of his hot and cold reputation among some. He traces it to the phone call he had with Dean Harwood back in 1968 when Harwood offered him a job. Harwood asked what he wanted as a title. Eelkema said, "How about professor and chairman?" Harwood agreed. The trouble is, at a university, the title of professor is one of those sacred rankings that one achieves only after much time and publication, progressing first through the steps of instructor and assistant professor. Suddenly the brash Bob Eelkema was a professor on equal footing with the academic elite. Forever after, says Wally Nelson, Eelkema was seen as "an outsider."

Another mark against him was his track record at securing grants. Grant writing seemed rather lowbrow to many. But no one could scoff at his success: working out of a tiny office at the medical school that had once been a washroom, Eelkema and his assistant, Sue Huus, generated about $30 million in various grants in a ten-year period.

"I always made my own money when I was head of the department of community medicine," says Eelkema. "I never had to go to the dean's office for money. It kept me secure. But it got to people who were academically inclined."

Finally, there was the added taint of his lowly status as a public health doctor. Just as with military fliers, if you're not a Top Gun jet pilot you're nothing. So, too, with doctors. If you're not a fast-lane surgeon, many feel you're beneath them. The lowest rung on the totem pole for many doctors is the Public Health Service, with its low glamour, low wages and low show-off potential.

But at least one of Eelkema's colleagues laughs at such pettiness. Dr. George Magnus Johnson's career as a brilliant pediatrician specializing in diabetes included a stint as an epidemiologist at the Centers for Disease Control and Prevention in Atlanta. If it hadn't been for a thick-headed journal editor, Johnson's theories about an unusual outbreak of disease in North Carolina that killed children would today be called Johnson's Syndrome and not Reye's Syndrome (See Chapter Twenty Two).

At any rate, Johnson sees Eelkema's career in public health as a brilliant one, though acknowledging that it was probably not just his chosen medical specialty that drew the occasional harrumph from a colleague.

"Bob's a real character," smiles Johnson. "Sometimes more so than needed. He rankles people almost on purpose. But that's Bob and I've known Bob all my life. He's almost like a brother to me. Bob's positives far outweigh his negatives. I'd hope someone would say that about me."

Clifford, of course, has heard it all about his old handball partner.

"Bob was Bob," he says. "Yes, he had a real knack for going after grants. But he was a master at getting that medical school project going. I just think we'd have never had the school without him."

In late June, as the deadline for submitting the AHEC application approached, Eelkema met with Clifford to get final authority to submit it. He, Nelson and Vennes were preparing to fly to Washington to hand-deliver their package. At the last minute, Clifford scrawled out an impromptu — and extremely rare — memo on a sheet of university stationary. It said, "Special emissaries to the president," and was followed by his signature.

In Washington, Eelkema led his group to the AHEC grant office. They were met by some well-meaning functionary who brightened at the sight of them. He said, "So, how are things in Raleigh?"

Wally Nelson just about flipped his cowboy hat he was so mad at the slight. He even got out a map of the United States and pointed out to the bureaucrat the difference between North Carolina and North Dakota. It wasn't the best of omens. Neither was the onset of Hurricane Agnes, raining cats and dogs as the trio left the AHEC office for National Airport. Flights there were being canceled, and what had begun as a hopeful trip had now bogged down in thunder and lightning. But then the boys from Raleigh caught a break: they boarded their flight home and took off just as the rain-saturated airport shut down completely.

Back in Washington, Doug Fenderson admits, he took a strong interest in the North Dakota application, and Clifford's support. Not enough to try to fix the process in favor of the North Dakotans, he is clear to point out. But enough to watch carefully as their application moved through the bureaucracy.

"I consider myself only a footnote to this story," says Fenderson. "I simply administered some of the sections of the AHEC law that related to the needs of North Dakota. A lot of my staff didn't even know where North Dakota was."

Without him there to guide the staff, though, it's clear that the proposal might have slipped through the cracks. Each grant was assessed by a council of outside reviewers. They lacked first-hand knowledge of any of the proposals, meaning Fenderson's staff support was a key factor. His staff did some initial background work on each application and issued a report to the review council.

"The staff guidance that went into the review process could have weakened the North Dakota application," Fenderson admits. "I thought it was a proposal a lot of reviewers would not understand. You had some high-toned academics sitting on the review councils and they didn't understand the Midwest. If I thought it was a dumb idea, there were ways I could have influenced it. But the support the North Dakota plan got from my office was strong support. I had great respect for Eelkema. He was a plainspoken, direct person. He didn't play games. I was that kind of person, too. And his program fell exactly in the center of what was being talked about — problems of maldistribution in both rural and inner city areas. There was some concern it would be an atypical AHEC. My view was that North Dakota's plan was just the kind of thing this law was intended to support. One had to take problems as they existed, not the way they were preconceived by someone else. Their plan fit right into the essence of what AHEC was all about."

Still, as important as Fenderson's support was at the very beginning, he would have little influence over the final outcome. The Bureau of Health Manpower had limited funds in its first year, with enough to approve only eleven programs. The competition for those dollars, says Fenderson, was stiff.

"By no means was it a shoe-in for any of them. Some medical schools were asking for the grant to increase the size of their school, others wanted to use it for nurse training programs. There was a great deal of ferment in that era."

The Mole

15

As they waited anxiously for word on their AHEC proposal, the Chuck House Gang found lots of help that summer of 1972 in spreading their message to the rural parts of the state. Many of the doctors who had sided with the majority in the Medical Association's May vote were pitching in to persuade their local legislators and neighbors. Clifford, in fact, saw that May vote as producing a benefit others hadn't grasped.

"I knew we'd have doctors out there who would be great PR people for us if we ever had budget problems. They would help get the vote."

That network was critically important, says Earl Strinden. "Nobody is more effective talking to a citizen legislator about what is important for North Dakota's future on health care than the family physician. Out on these great windswept prairies, the old family doctor holds an esteemed position. They are there through blizzards and the worst of storms. I'm not too sure people who live in a different climate understand the important role of the country doctor."

Even so, as the May vote had suggested, not every doctor liked the idea of a four-year medical school. So Eelkema, as chairman of Clifford's Chuck House Gang, figured the best person to convince a doctor was another doctor.

In Bismarck, for example, Phil Dahl, Keith Foster and Grandon Tolstedt led the attack on reluctant physicians and legislators.

"What happened," remembers Foster, a Bismarck internist, "there was a group of doctors who just stepped up and said this is what we're gonna do. They were people

like Grandon Tolstedt, people who were farsighted. They just told the other doctors if you don't want to come along, fine. But we're going to do this. They were putting in the extra time and effort, and rallied the support. They saw what had to be done. They weren't thinking of their own pockets."

Tolstedt, now retired and living in Little Rock, Arkansas, remembers some hot debates. "We flew all over the state and gave lectures to guys in practice," he says. "That was okay, except it wasn't always well received. These doctors thought, 'I know just as much as that guy from Bismarck.'"

By and large, recalls Harlan, most of the discussions were marked less by contentiousness than suspicion.

"I didn't see them passionate one way or the other," says Harlan. "They were sort of doubting. 'Why here?' they'd ask. 'You tell us to do these things, why are you doing that? What's going on here? The last person who came in and gave me a spiel like this swindled me with equipment that wasn't any good. You're selling something here. What is it you're selling?' That sort of thing."

The really hot and spicy arguments were concentrated for the most part in one familiar corner of the state. "Minot was with us," recalls Phil Dahl. "Bismarck was with us. Grand Forks was with us. Dickinson, Williston. It was Fargo that was the problem. It was kind of a turf battle like it always is."

Dahl had his trial by fire when he spoke before the Medical Association's district society in Fargo — the largest in the state.

"Some of my closest friends in the medical profession took right after me," he recalls. "They just didn't feel that was the way to do it. 'And you tell me why,' they'd say. That included one of my best friends, Buck Lamb, a plastic surgeon. He and I hunted together just about every year. He was a great guy, a terrific surgeon. A good hunter, terrific shot. But, God, he was one of the toughest questioners. He wasn't for the program. He got up and said, 'You dumb bastard.' I knew I was in trouble when I went in there."

"They ganged up on us at Fargo," adds Wally Nelson with none too pleasant a taste still in his mouth. "I was down there several times. It was hard. They threw me out, that's the way I felt."

Even the golden charm of Tom Clifford couldn't persuade the hard core of Fargo.

"The other day I was at a lunch with Judge Wolper," he recalled recently. "He was a great opponent of the medical school when he was in the Legislature back then, representing Fargo. I saw him and we talked. I told him I knew he had voted against it. He said, 'Yeah, Tom, I did. But I'll never forget when you gave the speech about the young kids getting a medical education. I almost voted for it.'"

Yet, even in Imperial Cass, there were those doctors who dared think differently.

"Some of us felt very strongly about this school and what it did for young people in particular and what it did for the state and what it meant to the state," says Dr. George Magnus Johnson, a UND graduate, who has practiced in Fargo most of his life. "The quality of the two-year medical school had been there over the years and it had always been one of the stars in the crown of UND. But these doctors said the school's got to close. They said it was impossible for this dinky, podunky medical school to maintain itself."

Many of the opponents, he recalls, were close to retirement. "But some of them were just outright sore-minded. The lack of generosity, the lack of willingness to look at young people's needs just wasn't there."

Johnson tried to act as a go-between, arranging for UND officials to meet with Fargo doctors and legislators. "But it was difficult," he recalls. "I was a bit on the hot seat in Fargo. I was this young guy supporting the medical school. I just felt that it had to be. I wasn't there to pick a fight with the old guys, but they made it very unpleasant. They got downright nasty and belligerent, especially these old guys who didn't want to commit any time or effort. And without having an open mind, they just said, 'The school doesn't belong here; close it.'"

Several times, Johnson arranged for John Vennes to come into Fargo to give a talk and answer questions. Vennes had taught Johnson during his own UND days, and everywhere else in the state he was treated with deference.

"But he was treated here in a most atrocious and unprofessional and abysmal way," says Johnson. "No cordiality. That should be a basic part of life, especially living here. If you don't have it here, where are you going to have it? But he took the rudeness like a gentleman, He didn't fire back with mean mindedness."

C. Warner Litten, now retired, doesn't recall any bitter arguments. "They were somewhat leery about expanding the school," is the way he describes doctors' feelings back then. Litten was the man who ran the Fargo Clinic — now renamed Merit Care — and also served as majority leader of the State Senate.

"They weren't against a four-year school, but they thought we ought to be careful," he says. "One of things that bothered them was that they didn't think there was enough of a population base in Grand Forks to give these young, aspiring physicians the kind of clinical material they need to learn a real practice."

George Johnson shakes his head, saying quality was not the only issue behind the Fargo opposition.

"There's always been resistance to medical student education in Fargo," he says. "It came out in 1972 during our regular clinical meetings. People would say, 'Ah the hell with that medical school in Grand Forks. Stay away from it. We don't want any involvement. It's gonna cost us time and money. That's not what we're here for.' They didn't want to be involved. They were in power, they were older, they'd been in a stable place for a long time. Not many had gone to UND. And therein lies the problems. They didn't have the feelings that the rest of us did. They felt they were the power and Grand Forks was up there and we're the institution that counts and all the rest of you are Podunk. In other words, Imperious Cass. It was a force to be reckoned with. To say the least, the meetings were passionate. Fiery."

Clifford was able to distance himself from the hottest debates in Fargo.

"It was an aggravating factor," he says, "but it wasn't a major obstacle."

No? What about Litten?

"Warner Litten was a very smart, good guy," says Clifford. "He really opposed the school. He was the manager of the Fargo Clinic. They were just protecting it. We were both protecting our own self-ish interests. I never held any grudges. They did what they thought was right, we did what we thought was right."

But what was right wasn't without its complications or its strata-gems. Because in Clifford's mind, what was right was to go after the most influential doctor in Fargo — perhaps in the entire state — and simply make him an offer he couldn't refuse.

That doctor was Lee Christopherson.

A poor boy from Bemidji, Minnesota, Christopherson had emerged from his training at the Mayo Clinic as a supremely gifted neurosur-geon. He settled in Fargo, a city with two competing clinics. He joined neither, preferring to start his own — the Neurosurgery Institute. In 1972 he was the state's only neurosurgeon. He had a strong referral base and therefore a great deal of influence among doctors.

And so far he hadn't taken any real position on the idea of creating a four-year medical school.

"We knew that Fargo was a hard nut to crack," says Eelkema, "but Lee Christopherson represented the perfect fulcrum."

Clifford smiles at the memory of Christopherson. "He was well respected, but not especially liked," he says. "And he didn't give a damn about what anybody said."

Naturally, Clifford knew him, but the story of how they met — long before any of this came to be — says something about the way Clifford himself thought about what anybody said.

It happened while Clifford was dean of the business school. A student came to ask his advice. He told Clifford that his father was a doctor and wanted him to follow in his footsteps. In fact, the father insisted on it. The only problem: the young man didn't want to be a doctor. He was interested instead in business school.

"I told him I'd put him in the business school that semester," Clifford remembers. "He says, 'My dad ... ' And I interrupted him. I said, 'Tell your dad to go to hell. This is your life.'

"A few weeks later at a cocktail party in Bismarck, a tall skinny baldheaded guy came over to see me. I didn't know who he was. He said, 'You're Tom Clifford, right?' I said, 'Yes, I am.' He said, 'Is it customary for you to advise your students to tell their parents to go to hell?' I laughed and said, 'You must be Christopherson.' And we became very good friends. We had a good relationship. The kid got through his business classes, by the way, and then he became a doctor. Life has a lot of peculiar twists."

The Chuck House Gang invited Christopherson to Grand Forks that summer and met him at the medical school. Clifford was not there, preferring to let his cabinet handle the negotiations. Eelkema, who was there, says they asked Christopherson point blank: what would it take to get you to support us?

"He didn't have to think about it," says Eelkema. "He wanted to be chairman of the neurosurgery department in the new medical school. So we made him the chairman."

Christopherson had another condition. He wanted all other medical school department chairmen recruited from North Dakota doctors first. If none wanted those jobs, then they should find North Dakota grads outside the state. And if that search failed, only then could they hire complete outsiders for the key medical school jobs. That made perfect sense to Eelkema and the others. With that, the deal was done.

"Then he was the mole," smiles Clifford. "He was our guy. It made a huge difference. Not only because of his excellence, but because of his position in Fargo. He was one of the pillars of their medical community."

And although not even Christopherson could change the minds of some of his colleagues, his support for the medical school neutralized much of the anti-medical school sentiment with legislators.

"Lee Christopherson was an extraordinary human being," says George Johnson. "I remember when he did a neurosurgery on my neck. I had a bad, herniated disc. Lee was the first one I recognized when I woke up after surgery. He was standing there. That's the kind of guy he was. He knew all the family doctors in the state. He knew how to deal with them. He was a medical politician par excellence. Through the force of his personality — force is the right word to use — he founded TNI in Fargo. He was the kind of man who could stand up and say, 'Damn you bastards, the medical school is going to stay here and to hell with all your crap.' And that's what he did. He was so strong and so powerful and so respected that he could get by with that. None of the rest of us could. They would have tarred and feathered me, and thrown me out the window. But he said there will be a medical school and you people can just go to hell. And if it hadn't been for him, I wonder if we would have made it."

Calling
the Pope

16

Even though the AHEC advisory committees and their chairmen were operating now in each of the state's large cities, there was yet a missing ingredient. That was a unifying sense of confidence among the leaders that they could really pull this thing off. While Eelkema and Gary Dunn had told the Bureau of Health Manpower in no uncertain terms that the program was workable, at the same time the Chuck House Gang was scrambling to find a program somewhere in the country that resembled what it was North Dakota wanted to do. Because even they were wondering just how deeply over their own heads they had gotten themselves.

Leave it to Gary Dunn to find that program and reassure the Gang — and to set in motion one of the heartiest parties in the entire saga of the medical school campaign.

It turned out that Dunn knew several of the deans in the medical school at Michigan State in East Lansing. Michigan State had created something it called a medical school without walls. Medical students were sent to the hospitals in far-flung cities of upper Michigan, where they were trained by local physicians. In early June 1972, Dunn made some calls and arranged for a two-day series of lectures and seminars in East Lansing for a North Dakota contingent. All they had to do was get there.

No problem for Eelkema, whose close friend John Odegard had plenty of airplanes.

Eelkema contacted each AHEC group and asked them to select a state legislator, a physician educator, a hospital administrator, and some other significant person in their area who would take part in the Michigan State seminar.

In late August, Odegard sent out several of his smaller planes to places like Minot and Bismarck to pick up these dignitaries and fly them back to Grand Forks. Awaiting them on the tarmac was the flagship of the UND air fleet: a rickety looking, previously owned DC-3, of the type that rock and roll bands often leased and then flew into a cornfield, becoming instantly both late and great.

A photograph of the twenty passengers who climbed aboard that day shows that none seemed too worried about the type of aircraft. Each seemed excited about the adventure they were embarking on. Among the group were several of the usual suspects: Eelkema, Vennes, Bill Harlan, Wally Nelson. Even Ted Harwood had agreed to go along.

Representing officialdom were Art Bunker, the Speaker of the House; Oscar Solberg and Brynhild Haugland, of the interim committee of the Legislative Council; Peter Hinricks, the president of the Board of Higher Education, and Jack McDonald, the Board's legal counsel.

The four AHEC deans were in the group: John Magnus from Fargo, Grandon Tolstedt from Bismarck, Dick Larsen of Minot, and Bill Krech of Grand Forks. Others included were Dr. Phil Dahl and Vern Wagner from Bismarck; Dr. Dan Goodwin, a family practitioner from Grand Forks — his mother had been one of Bob Eelkema's first patients; Dr. Dick Johnson, a radiologist from Rugby (and cousin to

George); and Sister Johanna, the nun who ran St. Alexis Hospital in Minot. Rounding out the group was Jerry Skogly, UND's vice-president of finance. He went because everything that had to do with the medical school had to do with money.

As the group boarded and took their seats, John Odegard, seeing them off from the tarmac, handed Eelkema several bottles of booze. Eelkema and John Vennes then strapped on aprons and party hats and moved to the back of the plane where they set up a makeshift bar.

Once aloft, almost everyone crowded toward the back of the plane. The pilot, a brave soul named Knox, kept shouting for them to sit down. The tail of the plane was sliding across the sky and he couldn't steer.

"It was an unforgettable trip," says Harlan. "I know how to isolate people now and get their attention. Put them on an old DC-3, flying into a headwind. I think our ground speed was eighty miles an hour. There was lots of booze and a little bit of food. It was crazy."

Not long into the flight the plane ran into a severe thunderstorm. Most of the passengers didn't notice, says Eelkema. "It was a jovial celebration. We had pretty much everybody three sheets to the wind by the time we got to our first stop, which was Green Bay, Wisconsin."

That's the way Dr. Dick Johnson remembers it. "The mood was all upbeat all the time," he recalls. "It was just a good time. I was a young radiologist. When we landed in Green Bay for refueling, there was this phone. Someone picked it up and dialed home and connected. Quite a few people, somewhat giggly, decided I'm going to do that, too. You could dial anywhere."

In fact, someone in the group shouted, "Let's call the Pope!" Clifford, who wasn't along for the ride, remembers that call pretty well because the Green Bay Airport sent him the long distance bill.

"No one was feeling any pain," says Eelkema. "When we got to East Lansing that night, there wasn't a sober one among them. Everyone just sort of poured off. Tom Johnson, a dean from Michigan State, was there to greet us and he couldn't believe how happy everybody was when they got off the plane."

By the next morning everybody had sobered up, or so the story goes. They spent two days touring the medical school without walls, talking to doctors and administrators and faculty.

"We all thought it was wonderful," says Dick Johnson.

"The feedback we got in those meetings," adds Dahl, "supported and enhanced the view that by golly we could do it. We hadn't been 100 percent certain that we could do it before we went. It certainly reinforced us. We came back and worked even harder."

Wagner was among those impressed. "There had been a question of how the school would work. We met with the people in East Lansing and they demonstrated quite well that you can have a campus here and there and that it works very well. I think a lot of doubts were erased."

It did even more than that, says Harlan.

"The theme of that trip was, 'Look, we're going to show you some doctors who are practicing in communities in Michigan who have been doing this for five or six years and are doing it well. And they're gonna look just like you. And you're going to look just like them.' And I think they came back with a feeling that, 'Hey, they're not terribly different than me.' I think it was an important trip in getting the docs' confidence that they weren't talking about something that was second class. There's a real fear in North Dakota of doing anything second class. If they're gonna do it, they want to do it right. They had to see that a system like Michigan State's was high quality and that a state like Michigan could make it work. I think politically it brought people together."

John Vennes said much the same in an archival interview with Eelkema a few years later.

"Michigan State was a very pivotal point in the whole process. I have an idea there's a little bit of North Dakota mystique involved in all these things. If you can take somebody from North Dakota to some place that looks like it's better than or equal to some institu-tion they think is okay, and if you can show them that North Dakotans are okay, then you've created instant credibility for North Dakota. I think the visit to Michigan State did that."

Clifford, of course, was elated. He even paid the Pope's phone bill without much complaint. Recalling it years later, he can only chuckle. "They put them in an airplane — all of those leaders — and flew them down to East Lansing. They got 'em drunk and had a good time, just had a hell of a time selling them. Everybody came back real disciples. We now had grassroots support all over the state. The issue was never in doubt. But, thank God, the damn thing didn't crash."

Of course, that may have been what the call to the Pope was all about.

"Bobby, What Are You Doing?"

17

Bob Eelkema served up a large helping of good news at breakfast in the Chuck House in July. The AHEC grant proposal had gotten a positive review from the Division of Health Manpower. They were sending a three-man team of field inspectors to Grand Forks to review the proposed budget.

The review took place in the board room next to Tom Clifford's office — the three Washington bureaucrats, Dunn, Eelkema and Ruth Morgan, who was UND's director of grants and contracts. As the visiting inspectors watched, Dunn and Eelkema were up and down at a chalkboard all during that first day, jotting proposed budget additions and deletions. Ruth Morgan sat in back cranking the numbers on an old-fashioned adding machine. Eelkema says that as they went over every line in the proposed budget, they kept expecting to get some sense from the inspectors as to whether the budget was too high and, if so, how high. But the only signal they got was the vague and negative body language they read from their reviewers. Things didn't seem to be going well at all.

"We just weren't getting any where that first day," says Eelkema. "We were absolutely at loggerheads, not getting to first base. And they weren't telling us what we were doing wrong. They were just sort of beating around the bush and we didn't know where the hell we were going."

In a sense, the chickens were coming home to roost. For the budget numbers that Dunn and Eelkema had submitted weren't really based on anything from experience.

"Gary and I budgeted the damn thing. We turned it in for millions of dollars over several years. Bill Harlan gave us some ballpark figures for faculty, travel, equipment and salaries. But we kind of pulled the figures out of the air."

Once again, though, Dunn rose to the occasion. After that first session, he invited the trio from Washington to dinner, luring them with intriguing tales of the most famous bar in North Dakota — or almost North Dakota. Whitey's Wonderbar, with its art deco interior and well-known horseshoe shaped bar was actually just across the Red River in East Grand Forks, Minnesota. Whitey's had been a popular college hangout since the days of Prohibition, and a visitor from the East couldn't very well visit the area without a stop.

Eelkema says he and Dunn got their first inkling that the invitation had been a good move when one of the three bureaucrats oohed and ahhed over Whitey's eclectic menu. Among the offerings was the old-fashioned special "Finn and Haddie," another name for Finnan Haddock, the salted, smoked fish popular in Scotland and Ireland. For some reason it struck a responsive chord in one of the heretofore unresponsive bureaucrats.

"We drank a lot of beer that night, and some martinis," says Eelkema. "We gave them plenty of joy juice and after dinner we started giving them a tour of the East Side and Grand Forks."

Their first stop was directly across the street from Whitey's at the old Spud Bar. As they approached, Dunn turned to the three men and said, "You know, it's a rough bar. You may see a fight. So be careful when you walk in."

Just as they opened the door, an unfortunate patron was getting popped in the mouth, and knocked out the door right in front of them.

"These guys were all from the East," laughs Eelkema, "and they'd never been West. This was really excitement for them, this little bit of the frontier in the Wild West. They were enjoying every minute of it."

Later in the bar, as Gary Dunn downed boilermakers to their delight, the leader of the Washingtonians leaned over to Eelkema.

"You know, we like you guys," he said, "and we want you guys to get this grant. But you're not going to get it with the money you're requesting."

Both Dunn and Eelkema were immediately sober.

"Is that right?" said Eelkema.

"The only way you can do it," said the grant man, "is to reduce your budget by $500,000."

Dunn and Eelkema exchanged knowing glances.

Early the next morning "with a little bit of a hangover," says Eelkema, he and Dunn talked things over. "If they hadn't let slip that we needed to cut half a million, the next day we probably would have insisted on getting all of our money. But they didn't telegraph that to us the first day. The fact they did that night was something they probably shouldn't have done."

In the morning, Eelkema and Dunn were in agreement.

"We thought we'd rather have something than nothing at all," says Eelkema. "We knew we had padded the budget considerably. That had been Gary Dunn's experience. He said if you don't ask, you don't get. We had doctor salaries and administrative officer salaries and secretaries. We cut the administrative officers right away. We had a position called dean of allied health. It was supposed to coordinate nursing and physical therapy and medical technology. All of those programs had already told us they didn't want anyone coordinating them. So that left the budget real quick."

The two men worked feverishly at the blackboard in the conference room next to the president's office. They started scratching out line items left and right, sometimes slicing out fairly large chunks.

As they did, Ruth Morgan sat in the back, aghast. She hadn't been there the night before and didn't understand what was happening. Up until then she had been politely referring to "Dr. Eelkema" and he to "Mrs. Morgan."

Now, though, her jaw dropped as Dr. Eelkema lopped off another $20,000.

"Bobby," she loudly exclaimed. "What are you doing?"

The three red-eyed bureaucrats turned around in their chairs and stared at her. They, too, didn't know what was happening.

"Oh, don't mind her," said Eelkema breezily. "I used to sleep with her."

Now the three men turned sharply to the front, amazement registering in their eyes.

"Until my mother kicked her out of bed when I got to be a teenager," Eelkema added. "She's my sister."

A big belly laugh, then. A real tension-breaker and a connection back to the good times of the night before.

"I think they kind of enjoyed that," says Eelkema. "I think we got more money out of them because of that. By the time they left they were saying, 'We're going to help you out.'"

But the final word on whether their AHEC grant was approved wouldn't come until the end of September. In the meantime, Oscar Solberg's interim Medical Education Committee held its second meeting on September 7.

The last thing it had officially heard in January was that doctors were opposed to the idea of a four-year school — or, at least, skeptical of it — and the Medical Association was going to put it to a vote in May.

The first man to speak at the September hearing was the newly recruited Fargo mole, Dr. Lee Christopherson. In no uncertain terms he came across as a strong advocate of the expansion, stressing that the medical school would feed the growth of the entire medical industry in North Dakota and also give young people the opportunity to become doctors.

This was quite a turnaround from the first meeting where one of Christopherson's lesser colleagues from Fargo had said most doctors were opposed. One thing Christopherson admitted, however, was that more doctors would likely be positive if they knew exactly how much of their time they'd need to spend with medical students.

Eelkema handled that concern during his remarks in which he also brought the committee up to date on the proposal for the AHEC grant; its time estimates were under review now by the AHEC staff in Washington. Eelkema also told the committee of the work of the medical affairs committee — aka Clifford's Chuck House Gang. Since June the MAC had held twenty informational meetings in the four proposed AHEC cities.

Bill Harlan then made his first appearance before the committee, assuring them that the proposed budget contained "no frills or fancy stuff," and was organized around people and not new buildings. He also noted that the state was eligible for a Pell grant — named after Rhode Island Senator Claiborne Pell. It was a one-time grant that would bring in an estimated $3.2 million over a three-year period. By the way, he noted, the class that had just entered the two-year medical school at UND numbered sixty-three students. The competition for those slots had been the most intense ever, with 450 applications.

In the afternoon session, the committee heard from each of the four doctors who were heading the temporary AHEC advisory groups in Minot, Bismarck, Grand Forks and Fargo. But if the committee thought everything was now copasetic with the state's doctors, it got an abrupt challenge.

In spite of Christopherson's intimidating prestige, Dr. Lester E. Wold of Fargo raised again the hoary old issue of there not being enough patients or large enough clinical facilities in North Dakota to adequately train medical students. After some time spent batting that old chestnut around, one of the more surprising witnesses got up to testify.

Peter Hinrichs was the president of the all-important Board of Higher Education. Clifford hadn't officially asked the Board for its support and it hadn't offered any. At first, Hinrichs's comments seemed mildly supportive of the medical school.

"The citizens on main street," he said, "are extremely concerned about the quality of medical services available to them because it directly relates to their quality of life." But, he cautioned, whether or not the medical school would expand would come down to what the State Legislature felt it could afford to have or not have.

Committee member Evan Lips then put the key question squarely to Hinrichs. Will the Board of Higher Education make a recommendation on the four-year medical school? It was a key question, but also a bit of subterfuge. Clifford didn't want to ask this question himself for fear of the answer. Getting Lips, his ally, to pose it, would at least give him a hint as to how the Board was really leaning. In answer, however, Hinrichs was vague, saying only that the Board would probably consider that option at its October meeting.

This prompted committee member Brynhild Haugland to issue a short lecture on how the one-mill levy that was passed in 1948 for the medical school "implied that it would result in more physicians being available in North Dakota. It's time to deliver on this implied promise."

Again, it was exactly the kind of message Clifford wanted to send the Board — although not from his own lips. But rendered by a most powerful member of the Legislature, it was a message Hinrichs heard clearly, and carried back to rest of his Board.

One might expect that the final decision on UND's application for an AHEC grant would be big news in North Dakota. With so much at stake for the medical school, the university and the state as well, it might even qualify as the medical story of the year. But on September 30, when the word came through from Washington that the $2.6 million grant had been approved, most daily newspapers in the state for some reason buried a three-paragraph version of the story in their back pages. Only *The Minot Daily News* seemed to grasp the significance of what had occurred, giving the story major play.

But if editors across the state were bored by what they considered a routine announcement, the news generated immediate excitement at the university, in the medical association, in doctor's offices across North Dakota and, of course, at the Westward Ho.

First of all, the grant meant the university wouldn't have to ask the State Legislature for more money than it had received in the previous budget. In fact, the grant was even better than the one-time Pell grants. It would renew every year for ten years, satisfying a vexing concern of the Legislature: who's going to pay for this in the years to come?

"I don't think we could have done it without that AHEC grant," says Vern Wagner, "because the Legislature looked very hard at money. For a small state, we have a pretty sophisticated higher education system. We were concerned that we couldn't afford much more."

But even beyond the money, the grant laid a heavy stamp of approval on the community medical school idea. All those tiresome complaints about no big university hospital and not enough patient material being available were now moot points.

"The AHEC was the only thing that made sense for a rural state," noted Em Murray at the Legislative Council. "It seemed to insure the support of the medical community."

In Washington, meanwhile, Doug Fenderson was likewise pleased.

"I wasn't surprised," says Fenderson. "Much of the credit goes to the doctors of North Dakota who had a concern for health care in the state that transcended their own personal practices. If it wasn't for that strong base of support from the practicing community and Bob Eelkema's leadership — it wouldn't have gone at all."

For Clifford's Chuck House Gang, news of the approval meant the real work was about to begin. Exacting details now were required for every aspect of the AHEC system. Bill Harlan was at work on those while Eelkema turned toward the huge job of finding the right people to run each AHEC office.

"We got the go ahead from AHEC to go out and start recruiting," he recalls. "And the first thing we wanted was to hire the permanent deans of each AHEC. They would then recruit the faculty from their areas. We also had to have chairmen of medicine, surgery, pediatrics and so on in each AHEC."

He spent much of his time in the early days going to meetings of the American Medical Association and the North Dakota Medical Association, interviewing candidates. Under the agreement the medical school had made with Lee Christopherson, Eelkema needed first to recruit from in-state UND grads and then out-state grads and then the general population of doctors in the nation. But finding doctors for chairmen turned out to be much harder than he'd thought.

In all of their recruiting in-state, only one doctor — Keith Foster, a Bismarck internist — was willing or qualified to take on the responsibility. The search quickly expanded outside the state, but it was clear that luring doctors to the forbidding climes of North Dakota was going to be a challenge. In the meantime, there was an urgency to the recruiting process. Before the Legislature would look kindly upon a four-year school, and before the American Association of Medical Colleges would grant even a temporary accreditation, the key people had to be in place. Without them — and even with the AHEC grant — the degree-granting medical school was still only theoretical.

What the situation required was a spellbinder, the kind of super

168

salesman who could sell a bikini to an Eskimo. Luckily there just happened to be such a man already in place. And very quickly Gary Dunn became, in Bob Eelkema's words, "the major domo of recruiting."

Even though he was himself an outsider, Dunn became the ultimate cheerleader for North Dakota. "A lot of North Dakotans have an inferiority complex about their state," says Eelkema. "But Gary didn't have any reservations about selling North Dakota. He was very devoted and committed to doing something good for North Dakota. And he brought in a lot of people. He recruited most of the AHEC deans, most of the chairmen. He was a real persuasive guy and he convinced a lot of people to come here. You have to give credit to a guy who persuades a doctor who could go anywhere to move to Minot, North Dakota."

That was the good news. The not-so-good news was the quality of many of those recruits.

"Gary was a master at talking people into coming, though the type of people who came were not always exactly stellar," says Eelkema. "We took less than adequate sometimes to get the positions filled. We were in a race to get accredited."

What does "less than adequate" mean?

"They were people in transition," says Nancy Dunn. "Scratch the surface and there was partnership discord, or they were running away from bad situations. Some came out here to make a last shot at a bad marriage. Almost always if we had our choice we'd recruit in January. We could say it doesn't get any worse than this and look at how much fun we're having."

Fun was one of the main things Dunn used to sell the state. He would stress the abundance of hunting and fishing opportunities in North Dakota. Although he had never been a hunter or a fisherman, it didn't stop him from buying a wardrobe of hunting clothes and a gun and taking batches of recruits hunting. "He didn't know what he was doing," says Eelkema, "but he did it."

Yet it is true, most of the recruits who signed on were somewhat suspect.

"Everybody was a renegade from somewhere else," says Eelkema. "They were either alcoholics or manic depressives or running away from an ex-wife. They were problem people. Who in the hell can you get to come to North Dakota to a situation that you aren't sure will survive? We ended up with a lot of deadbeats and crazy people. I can think of one doctor who ended up in prison for Medicaid fraud. There was another guy who used to have dead bodies from the medical school in the back of his car so he could do post mortems at home. A really crazy guy. We had guys that came and went, and we knew this would happen. Bill Harlan had told us that. He said any time you've got a new school and you're hiring new people, there's going to be a lot of storming and forming. There will be people who come in and make fools of themselves, not relate well and then leave. Then, we would start to replace them with North Dakota graduates and North Dakota people and they will be the ones who will settle in and it will be an institutionally positive school. He predicted right."

As the recruiting got under way, Eelkema was finding himself in a fix of a different kind. In addition to the AHEC grant, Doug Fenderson had told Eelkema about federal money available for medical projects involving minorities and Indians. Eelkema and Dunn then hit on the idea of creating a program that would pay for the medical school education at UND of a number of Native Americans. Nancy Dunn, typing up the proposal one night while her husband and Eelkema gabbed away, noticed the title they had attached to it: Indians into Medicine. She chopped it down to INMED. They loved the catchy acronym in Washington and immediately funded the project. In fact INMED today is responsible for training over twenty-seven percent of all the Native American physicians practicing in the United States.

But Eelkema, the grant guru, was suddenly the project director of three huge federal grants: MEDEX, AHEC and INMED. And he'd just won approval from the Department of Labor for a smaller grant involving health training. Once more, Ruth Morgan, his sister and the university's director of grants, had to shout, "Bobby, what are you doing?"

Federal regulations limit the amount of professional time a single individual can spend administering grants. But Eelkema was now, technically, spending 338 per cent of his time as project director, a violation of physics as well as federal law. Something had to give, said Ruth. Dunn therefore became the project director of AHEC, INMED was farmed out, and Eelkema actually returned the Department of Labor grant to the government. He kept MEDEX as his main federal responsibility.

Hedging
the Bet

18

Two weeks after the AHEC grant came through, Oscar Solberg's committee met again — this time in Grand Forks and this time in a rare, combined meeting with the Board of Higher Education. Things were heating up now in both the legislative process and in Clifford's grand strategy.

The first speaker that October thirteenth was Bob Eelkema. He stunned the audience when he announced that Clifford had hired the consulting firm of Booz, Allen & Hamilton to come to North Dakota and re-examine the entire four-year plan.

But why? They already had the "outside" Dunn Report that suggested it was the way to go. They had even quashed a minority report and solidified support among most of the members of Solberg's committee.

The why was simple. Clifford was the kind of man who never took anything for granted. Even as the good news was flowing in that summer, he had kept touch with Board of Higher Education members and state legislators and had picked up a vibration he couldn't ignore.

By now Gary Dunn had been to enough places in the state that some people were beginning not just to doubt his credentials and his supposed objectivity, but were getting vocal about it. The Dunn Report was beginning to be viewed as really an insider's report, and whatever credibility it had in getting the key vote of the Medical Association in May was disintegrating.

"So we had to get something that would sell," says Clifford. He went to the private Louis and Maud Hill Family Foundation and with $30,000 hired the prestigious firm of Booz, Allen & Hamilton.

This hedging of his bet came only moments before the heaviest assault yet on the proposal by the Fargo contingent — led by its chief naysayer, State Sen. C. Warner Litten.

Urging "a more cautious approach," Litten, the manager of the Fargo Clinic, questioned the backing the proposal really had among the state's doctors, and argued that too many questions had been raised about the plan's feasibility. Fargo doctors, he told the committee, needed convincing that every other avenue had been explored. No one he knew was against the program, he said, but no one seemed to favor it either. "Until more facts are in … slow down a little bit."

Litten cited a new report in the journal *Medical Economics* that soon there would be too many doctors in the country and therefore no new medical schools should be organized. He also seemed to address the credibility issue when he said, "There has not been enough study and too much emotion and urgency is being generated …. (There has been) a wild scramble to throw together statistics to justify a four-year school."

As for the AHEC grant, he brushed it aside, urging the committee and the Board not to be "sucked into a program simply by teaser money from the federal government."

Grandon Tolstedt fired back that "physicians always oppose

medical education proposals and medical schools, and five years from now we still won't have enough studies on this problem to suit some physicians."

But other doctors from Fargo rose to defend Litten's stand. One of them, Dr. G.H. Gall said he'd spoken personally to a vice-president at the University of Minnesota and was told there was no reason UM couldn't keep accepting transfers from UND. State Representative Art Bunker of Fargo urged another look at contracting UND students to other four-year schools.

Finally, George Sinner, the West Fargo member of the Board of Higher Education and future governor, sounded a note of gloom and hinted where his vote might lie. The proposal for the expanded medical school, he said, had to be judged on whether it would divert money from other education programs in the state.

Clifford himself addressed the controversy by saying that was exactly why he'd asked Booz, Allen to come in and look the whole project over.

Solberg gaveled the meeting to adjournment, with all agreeing to meet again as soon as Booz, Allen had turned in its report.

By now, Clifford and his Chuck House Gang had hoped the interim committee would have endorsed the four-year medical school and prepared legislation for the 1973 legislative session to adopt. But the necessity of bringing in a blue-ribbon consultant delayed the process another two months. It wasn't until December 15, only two weeks before the 1973 session opened, that the Solberg committee had a report in its hands.

Actually, when Solberg called to order the fourth meeting of his interim committee — this one back in Bismarck — the report was in the hands of the Board of Higher Education. Peter Hinrichs, the president of the Board, opened the meeting by stating that the Booz, Allen report was now the responsibility of the Board, even though UND had initiated the study. Knowing the ambivalence of the Board toward taking a stand on the medical school, many supporters were dismayed to see Hinrichs introducing the Booz, Allen team. Only Clifford, a close friend of Hinrichs, seemed untroubled.

The Booz, Allen study was called "Review of Alternatives for Medical Education in North Dakota." It began, much as the Dunn Report did, citing statistics on the poor patient-to-doctor ratio in North Dakota. In the past six years, it said the number of primary care doctors in the state had fallen off 13.5 per cent, which it termed "a severe decline in the number of physicians upon whom most people rely for entry into the health care delivery system."

The current medical school system, it warned, didn't meet the objective of increasing manpower. "The state has an obligation to its citizens," said the report, "to ensure the availability of adequate numbers of qualified health personnel."

So far, so good.

Like the Dunn Report, it noted that North Dakota had the highest percentage of its qualified students admitted to medical school in the nation.

And just as the Dunn Report had, it listed several options for action. In fact, four of the options were exactly the same as the Dunn Report: Phase out the school entirely? No, it said, that was counter to the state's obligation. Continue blithely to transfer students? No, that was impractical because transfers were about to stop. Create a medical school with adjoining states? No, it said. Too little evidence of any common ground. Contract with out-state medical schools? Here, the Booz, Allen report made its first veering-away from the Dunn Report. This wasn't a bad idea, it said. And finally, on the question of North Dakota's developing its own degree-granting medical school, it declared: "A good possibility."

But not a possibility without drawbacks. In some fairly dire language the report predicted "major problems," in developing a four-year school. A key problem, it suggested was the absence of residency programs in the UND plan. To really increase the likelihood that doctors from a four-year medical school would remain in North

176

Dakota, residency programs — post graduate studies beyond the fourth year of training — were a necessity, said the report.

"This is the single most important variable in recruitment of physicians," said the report. Residency programs, it emphasized, should be built into the AHEC Centers.

It wasn't that UND disagreed with this idea. In fact, Eelkema, Clifford, Willard Wright, Bill Harlan and others knew very well that an overwhelming percentage of new doctors decided to set up their practice within 100 miles of the place they completed their final residency program — not necessarily the place where they completed their fourth year. And without a residency program tacked onto the fourth year of medical school, those four-year grads were still likely to go out of state for post-graduate training and not come back.

The drawback as far as Clifford and others were concerned, was that asking for residency funding at the same time as asking for the four-year expansion would be too much for the Legislature to swallow in one bite. It had always been their plan to go back and get the residency funding once the four-year program had been passed.

Even as this first "major problem" and its proposed solution began to provoke discussion in the audience, it was quickly overshadowed by the stir that was caused when the report suggested what came to be known as the 2-1-1 plan.

The report said that the first two years of medical school should go on as usual at UND. For the third year, UND should contract with Minnesota's medical schools to take on its transfers at a price-per student to be negotiated with the Mayo Clinic and the University of Minnesota. An initial estimate figured about $11,000 per student. In the fourth year, the UND students would come back to North Dakota and be trained in the AHEC centers. Thus it was a 2-1-1 plan: two years in North Dakota, one year in Minnesota and one final year in North Dakota.

To staunch supporters of the medical school, this seemed to be caving in to the Fargo element.

For one thing, certain language in the report seemed to give away its source: "A number of national and local physicians and officials believe North Dakota will have difficulty recruiting residents in anything but family practice," it said, "because ... [medical school training] requires a critical mass of research ... drawing from a large enough population base to ensure breadth and depth of clinical material."

Just like that, an argument that had been dead and buried had come back zombie-like to haunt them.

Among the most distressed was Eelkema, Clifford's Chuck House chairman. He argued that the Booz, Allen investigators had talked only to Fargo doctors. And in specifically responding to the 2-1-1 suggestion, he recalls, "I pleaded with them not to do it. We needed that money to hire faculty. But, instead, we were going to enrich Minnesota. Their research funds were drying up and they were looking to us for some cash."

He didn't find much sympathy from Board members. Sinner said he "couldn't conceive of a four-year medical school in North Dakota being able to provide quality education for all the students enrolled in it." Vincent Buck, another Board member, added, "The proposals to date are too philanthropic to just one profession — the medical profession." He said the state would be spending a great deal of money with no assurance that physicians would ever return.

Tempers began to flare. Evan Lips lamented the large amount of money spent each year in North Dakota on liquor, cigarettes and state programs such as highway development, ignoring the really important issues such as medical care.

Bryce Streibel added his own howl. "Priorities are turned around," he said, "when North Dakotans will spend more for paving highways and roads than it will on providing medical education and services. If this continues, the state will see the day when a number of township and county paved roads go past empty farms on the way to the Twin Cities to enable citizens to get medical services."

When things began to settle down, the Solberg committee took a vote. It agreed with Booz, Allen's 2-1-1 idea and recommended legislation be adopted in the 1973 session to contract with Minnesota schools. It also recommended establishing residency programs. Finally, it ordered that the interim committee and Board appoint a panel to go to Minnesota and negotiate the cost of such a contract.

Because of the emotion at the meeting and because several concepts were brought up almost at once — the need for residencies, "major problems," sending students to Minnesota, not enough clinical material — news reports in the next days and weeks seemed to miss the point. Reports focused mainly on the watering down of the four-year medical school idea and not the notion that UND would now be able to grant medical degrees.

In fact, readers may have thought the whole idea was dead. The headline over the story of the meeting in *The Dickinson Press*, the following day read, "4-year school of medicine voted down." A column in *The Linton Record* a few days later said, "A Chicago consulting firm recommends against establishing a four-year medical school at UND ... " And a columnist for the *Pierce County Tribune* in Rugby wrote, "I was rather let down by the report of the Chicago firm which recommended that North Dakota not go for a four-year medical school."

Even the *Fargo Forum*, in a Christmas Eve editorial, seems to have missed the mark, suggesting that the Booz, Allen report "probably has ended any chance that the 1973 session of the Legislature will make the appropriations to start expansion of the UND two-year medical school to a four-year school."

In a more accurate report the day after the interim committee's vote, editor Jack Hagerty of *The Grand Forks Herald* captured the confusion and the anger:

> *"Bryce Streibel ... commented somewhat bitterly that it looked as if the Legislature might be more willing to spend*

money for animal health than for human health. He referred to a request in Gov. William L. Guy's budget for $1.7 million for a veterinary science building at NDSU ... also commented he had never seen such widespread support throughout the state for anything as had surfaced for a degree-granting medical college ....

The reaction to the report ... ranged from delight through relief to near anger .... Representatives of the UND medical school obviously were disappointed .... State Rep. Brynhild Haugland of Minot said it was 'a good report until it came to the conclusion.... Outside consultants are always saying something is not possible for North Dakota,' she said. 'It's discouraging to have people come in and pay them to tell you just can't do it .... I feel we're saying to the citizens of North Dakota that we are going to provide for their sons and daughters good law, pharmacy, accounting and other kinds of education, but sorry, we're not going to do anything for your son or daughter who wants to become a doctor.'"

In fact, the Booz, Allen 2-1-1 suggestion hadn't really killed the four-year plan at all, but made it more likely than ever that it would eventually pass legislative scrutiny one day. For the moment, though, the 2-1-1 plan felt to many like a defeat. And even that plan took a turn for the worse in following weeks.

Starting on January 9, 1973, Solberg's committee — which had met only four times in twelve months — met three times in thirteen days to second-guess itself about its earlier approval and to hammer out a final recommendation.

Two issues continued to vex the committee. One was the cost of paying Minnesota medical schools to take on UND students; the other was the cost of setting up residency programs. Neither cost had been figured in with all of the sweet rhetoric they'd heard over the past year about a four-year medical school. Suddenly, they were faced with a new bill for $600,000 to get the University of Minnesota and Mayo Clinic to take on forty third-year UND students. That figure came out of negotiations with those schools in late December by a committee made up of Clifford, Solberg, Vennes, Ken Rashcke and Dr. Bob Painter.

The one thing that made the $600,000 easier to accept was the idea that UND wouldn't have to spend more money paying for a third year of medical school in Grand Forks. It was more than a wash, they decided. It was actually cheaper to send the students away. One drawback, however: only forty students would be paid for. It left twenty-four graduates of UND's two-year school on their own to find medical schools that would accept their transfer.

At the interim meeting of January 9, that didn't seem to be a problem. The more they thought about it, committee members liked the 2-1-1 idea and agreed again that it was the way to go.

The other problem, however, was that the cost of residency training wouldn't be as easy to accept. They threw the ball back to Clifford's group, asking for a new budget that included everything. Another committee meeting was scheduled for January 19.

The interim committee was cutting it very close. The deadline for submitting proposed legislation for the 1973 session was Tuesday morning, January 23.

Presenting that revised budget to the committee that day fell to John Vennes. He estimated costs from 1973 through 1979. During those six years, the costs of the medical school would rise from $4.6 million to $9 million — with most of the increases coming from 2-1-1 tuition costs paid to Minnesota and the establishment of the fourth year of clinical training back in North Dakota.

But the proposed budget also included costs for establishing residency programs. These included salaries for a dean and an assistant dean, ten new full-time instructors, an estimated $11,000 for each of twenty-four resident students from 1976 on, various other personnel, travel and furniture expenses. The budget, he said, reflected the philosophy that UND would be the party responsible for funding residency programs and not the AHEC centers.

Those numbers immediately set teeth to grinding on the committee. Evan Lips, the loyal Clifford stalwart, led the expressions of dismay. He had no idea, he said, that the 2-1-1 plan proposed by Booz, Allen, meant the state had to pay for residency training. Vennes noted calmly that Booz, Allen had made it very clear that residency programs were a must. Vennes also noted that it would be cheaper in the long run to pay Minnesota to train both the third- and fourth-year UND students, except that Minnesota didn't want to do that. Even if it did, it wouldn't be feasible to have a residency program in North Dakota without its own four-year, degree-granting medical school.

But, asked Lips, couldn't residency programs be developed without financial help from UND? No, said Vennes. The doctors in the four AHEC regions had made it clear they expected UND to pay that bill.

Lips wasn't the only committee member upset by these unexpected, last-minute costs. Art Bunker, the Speaker of the House, said he was "very disappointed" in the budget, noting that it appeared the supposedly cheaper 2-1-1 plan would cost just as much as the original four-year plan.

Lips then left no doubt where the matter stood: he said he was no longer sure the Legislature would approve the plan. The solid support on the Solberg committee was wavering. None of the members wanted to recommend a bill to the full Legislature that would cost more than the appropriation given the medical school in 1971. At the moment, the high-minded ideals, the bonding on the trip to East Lansing, the desire to give their children a chance to go to medical school — all had faded. This being North Dakota, the issue was coming down to the bottom line.

Vennes and his colleagues were urged to draw up a new budget and present it to the committee at a meeting on Monday, only two days away.

For Vennes, and his Chuck House colleagues, it was a very hectic weekend. Everyone worked the phones, contacting doctors involved in each of the four AHECS, as well as hospital administrators, looking for support for those residency costs. By Monday a new plan had been cobbled together and this time Clifford himself settled into the witness chair before Solberg's group.

He essentially began by telling the committee that the budget presented last Friday had been a mistake. It had been based on erroneous assumptions, he said, that were the product of a communications failure, which was caused by tight deadline pressure. A simple human failure. While it wasn't exactly "my dog ate my homework," the excuse still might have sounded like clumsy tap dancing except that, when Clifford performed, it came off as the good old soft shoe.

Forget that budget, he said, here's the real one. No residency programs — they would now be handled by the private sector. The four AHEC chairmen said they would develop the residencies on their own and with the support of local hospitals. Best of all, the bottom line was now $1.1 million lower than Friday's bottom line.

The dance lasted only fifty-one minutes. Even Lips had heard what he needed to hear. He moved to recommend passage of the 2-1-1 program without residencies to the 43rd Legislative Session. Art Bunker seconded the motion and it passed unanimously.

And as it turned out, there was no need to worry about making the legislation deadline. The interim committee went calmly out of existence with nearly six hours to spare.

As Tight as They Come

19

The story of what happened next, as the bill moved through various legislative committees, is almost anti-climactic. A week later, the bill came up before the Senate education committee, and all it did was correct the spelling of the word "opportunities." Two weeks later, the bill passed the Senate by a 34–16 vote, with most of the no votes coming from Fargo.

Things went pretty much the same in the House, where it was brought to the floor on March 9. According to reporter Chuck Haga's account that appeared in the next day's *Bismarck Tribune*, the highlight of the House debate came when Representative Harley Kingsbury took the floor. The state's schools, he complained, "are constantly starting new programs." The Grafton Republican then asked plaintively, "What is sacred about education that we can't look at it and realize it's costing us too much? ... [I'm] not against education, but we're getting to the point where we can't support it."

The Kingsbury complaint — both its dogged attack on spending and its curious ambivalence toward educational growth — was

185

exactly the type of argument Clifford had worked so hard to deflect. When the House votes were counted, only twenty seven others sided with Kingsbury. The bill passed with seventy-one votes for the medical school.

By the way, Clifford is not alone among those who today believe the item that made the biggest difference in the home stretch was the Booz, Allen 2-1-1 plan. It was the kind of compromise that legislators love — they were able to vote for it but not all the way.

"With the 2-1-1 plan, you didn't have to commit yourself for the long haul," says Em Murray. "You could conceivably draw back if you had to. In the back of people's minds, there was hedging on a long-term commitment. We left our flank hanging in the air, to use a military term, and it meant our enemies could come in and torpedo the program. But no one really expected that to happen. It was cheaper to contract $11,000 a student for forty students because you didn't have to make quite the investment. I think there was a little disappointment from some supporters. But they got it so much further than they'd thought two years earlier."

Bill Harlan agrees.

"The 2-1-1 had to happen," he says. "It's impossible to suddenly start a medical school in a year or two and put people through the full range of things. Particularly when you have smart and demanding students. Eelkema was mad about the plan and so were some members of Solberg's interim committee. They felt as if a fast one had been pulled on them. They'd been sold on one idea, funded by AHEC. But now they were being told they'd have to pay money to the Mayo Clinic and University of Minnesota. To many of them it was another example of North Dakota money moving over to Minnesota. Wheat farmers always complained they got cheated by the millers over in Minnesota. And here was another example. And yet there was no other way to have done it."

That's what Clifford knew from the start.

"It's the way we had to go to get into it," he says. "I knew we

186

didn't have the quality of the faculty back then. We hadn't had the time to build it up. We had to recruit our faculty and get all our ducks in a row. We recruited some dogs the first year. They weren't the best. But we also had some of the best. I thought we had to be a little humble. Going back to my Marine Corps training, it's like taking an island. You take what you can and then you eventually get it all."

He says this with his standard Irish chuckle. And adds in a whisper, "You know the Booz, Allen report copied the Dunn Report right down to the errors in English and put their stamp on it. We took it into the Legislature and they said this is wonderful. This is marvelous. Oh, it was pure gold. It was the Booz, Allen name. It worked magic."

Yet even with the bill safely through the Legislature, Clifford had one more arm to twist. On March 19 the bill went to Governor Art Link for his signature. Ten days later he hadn't signed it. It was getting close to the time when the unsigned bill would actually die from what amounted to a pocket veto.

Clifford rushed to Bismarck.

"Art was a very conservative guy," says Clifford, "but a good guy. He was a really hard worker, and basically intelligent. He was of German extraction, always well intentioned and very honorable. If he told you he'd do it, he'd do it. We had a good relationship."

Clifford had helped Link raise money to run for Congress and had worked with him on economic development in the state. Once, before he was president, Clifford happened to be heading for the Williston area. Link asked him if he'd mind stopping in Alexander to check on the progress of an economic aid program Link had orchestrated.

"I went into the bar there, and said to the bartender, 'How are things going?'"

Not well at all, was the answer.

"I'll tell you, mister," said the barkeep. "A few years ago we had three bars in this town and we all were starving. Well, one guy quit and finally the other guy quit and finally I started making a living. And some son of a bitch from Bismarck came in and gave that other guy some money to start his bar and now we're starving again."

When Clifford walked in on his old friend that late March day in 1973, he was pretty sure Link would sign the bill. But he also knew he was having trouble with his conscience. Like Clifford, Link was a Democrat. But he was a conservative Democrat, a man with a social conscience, but also a man raised on the stark prairie outside Bismarck by immigrant parents.

That day in 1906 when they stepped off the train in Bismarck — his twenty-one-year-old father from the Sudetenland in Czechoslovakia, his eighteen-year-old mother from Bavaria — they knew nothing of farming. Yet they had taken the immigrant train, as had so many others, to North Dakota to homestead their own farm. And farmers they became — the only way they had of making their living.

It was rough going, but sometimes there was even room for laughter. Link likes to tell a story he heard repeated dozens of times when he was a boy growing up on that farm. His father had taken his meager life savings and purchased a pair of draught horses.

"My mother didn't know you needed a harness for the pair of horses that my dad bought," smiles Link. "He needed them to pull the plow. He said he had to buy a harness. She said what do you need a harness for? She told that story on herself. Another lady said to her, 'Do you think the horse could pull with its tail?'

"It's amazing how they adapted. If those homesteaders hadn't developed the skills to live off the land, ninety per cent of them couldn't have stayed. You couldn't make it on what you sold off the land. You ate what you processed and made. We had our own milk, our own meat, our own vegetables, potatoes. Everything you could raise. My folks raised a family of six kids, good and healthy. We drank all the milk we wanted. Baked our own bread. Butchered an animal or two through the year. We raised, beef, turkey, chicken. Those things were always in abundance. That's what gave our people opportunity to survive.

"But if you needed a piece of machinery, you had to pay cash for it. And nobody had much cash. So, in that case, everybody went in on a thrashing rig and worked together because there wasn't anybody could afford one. I think it's in the process of attempting to earn enough money to buy the things you had to have that you found a sense of belonging to the community."

Link's father had only a fourth-grade education when he got off the immigrant train, but he went to night school to learn English. He eventually became the clerk of the school district and treasurer of the township.

"Local government was a way of life," says Link. "It did the little things that had to be done. Like improving roads or hiring a teacher for the rural school I went to."

The sense of community, of sharing, along with the instinct for survival were seeds for a different kind of politics, he says. "We were conservative Democrats. As tight as they come."

Which is why, he says, by everything he was raised to believe in, he should have been against the great expenditure required to create a four-year medical school.

"I think there were too many people in the Legislature who said we can't afford it. We don't have enough people to support it. We don't need it here. But I was kind of on the opposite side of what you would expect of me philosophically and politically. A lot of people at that level can only think in terms of the dollar and nothing else. But I'd already developed the idea that the rural areas of our state were entitled to the same services as the larger communities."

In the days on his family farm, he remembers, "If the doctor did come at all, he didn't come until you called and said the baby's on its way can you get out here? There was more than one fatality because of that."

During the debates over expanding the medical school, Link says he began to agree that by sending medical students out of state, there was less of a chance that they'd come back and practice in North Dakota. His thoughts: "By golly, we want to keep our home-raised doctors and make it attractive for them to stay here."

And so Tom Clifford knocked on Link's door — you could do that then, walk right into the State Capitol and knock on the governor's door — and asked him what was the deal.

"I said, 'Art, you've got to approve that. It's on your desk.'"

"'God, Tom,' he said, 'it costs a lot of money.'"

Clifford prodded him along. "You knew that, Art. You came on the campus and you gave your word you were going to approve that."

Link nodded. Perhaps an image crossed his mind of struggling farmers trying to buy a thrashing machine.

"'Yeah,' he said. 'Okay. Let's get a student and a couple legislators and bring them. We'll have a picture.'"

Clifford wasted no time. He rounded up Evan Lips and Bryce Streibel, but couldn't find a single UND student anywhere in the State Capitol. But he did come across a young man in a Bismarck Junior College jacket.

"Fortunately," grins Clifford, "it was reversible. I had him turn it inside out and put it on."

And so the picture was taken. And Art Link kept his word and signed the bill. And Tom Clifford got clean away without ever asking for or getting the approval of the Board of Higher Education. And boys and girls across North Dakota started thinking maybe they'd become a doctor when they grew up. And Gary Dunn was on the phone telling some doctor back East that heck, it didn't really get that cold in North Dakota. It was, of course, a lot of bull.

No Question about It

20

During one of the last hearings held by Oscar Solberg's interim committee in 1972, when the Booz, Allen 2-1-1 plan was being favorably commented on, a Jamestown doctor named Evan Kostick raised his hand from the audience. He wondered aloud if UND students would get a quality education in their third year at the University of Minnesota or at Mayo Clinic. Both schools, he suggested, would have so many extra medical students that maybe the UND kids would get lost in the shuffle. It was a concern that drew little response from the politicians, although doctors like Bob Eelkema and Wally Nelson were worried about the same thing.

It wasn't until the end of the first year of the 2-1-1 plan that anyone really answered Dr. Kostick's question. Keith Foster, the AHEC dean in Bismarck and his colleague, Grandon Tolstedt, traveled to Minnesota to talk to the UND students.

"We were horrified," recalls Tolstedt. "They were given the poorest rotations. Separated from the rest of the students. They were not getting a good education. There were things going on that were not right."

When they came back, they spread the word. "There wasn't any evil-doing by the University of Minnesota," says Tolstedt, "but they had too many students to keep track of it. They took the money and ran, that was the sour feeling. We said this must cease."

And so as soon as the five-year 2-1-1 contract with Minnesota had expired, another campaign was begun and another interim committee headed by Oscar Solberg went back to revisit the medical school issue. But this time Tom Clifford had the help of a new Chuck House ally. Dr. Tom Johnson, the man who had watched Eelkema's inebriated army stumble off their plane at East Lansing seven years earlier, was now the dean of the UND medical school.

An avid collector of old Studebakers, Johnson used the pretext of searching out old car parts as an excuse for showing up on a rural legislator's doorstep on any given day to talk about this, that and, oh by the way, the medical school. "He was just masterful at being old shoe, down to earth," says Earl Strinden.

"Tom Johnson was my hero," adds Keith Foster. "I couldn't have had a better dean. You have to realize that the medical school isn't going to exist unless you've got support in the Legislature, because that's where the money comes from. And you can't go up to talk to legislators when they get into Bismarck and tell them what you want. There's all these other people coming in and telling them what they want. What Tom and I used to do was we'd go out and visit legislators in their own stamping grounds. So when they got in town they knew us. We'd drive out and have coffee in the front of a drugstore in, say Taylor, and then we'd go down to Richardton where a guy was feeding his cattle in a feedlot, and then we'd go down to Bowman and meet a guy in a beer parlor. One time we pulled into a filling station in Beech. The guy who was going to fill up my car said, 'Dr. Foster, what the hell are you doing out here?' Tom Johnson looked at me and said, 'Do you know everybody in southwestern north Dakota.?' I said almost.

By the time the legislative session of 1981 began, most of its members had been paid a friendly visit by Johnson.

"Tom was really the person who got this thing going," says Vern Wagner. "Tom had a lot of political savvy He went around to every single extremely rural place in the state to sit in the kitchen of every legislator. Tom was Tommy. He was just a wonderful person. He knew medical education backwards and forwards. But he could get along with anybody. Legislators loved him. He presented very well, he had a good sense of humor and he could talk with the most scientific physician or the janitor. He was the one who was able to bring the third year back. In the Legislature, you know by the way a person responds if they know what they're talking about. You sense it. And I can't emphasize it enough: Tommy did his homework."

Part of that homework was understanding who held the power in the Legislature. Johnson's mastery of that piece of the puzzle became clear not long after a Fargo legislator introduced a bill in the late 1970s to close the medical school. For even though the Legislature had already approved the expansion, some Fargo legislators refused to give up, raising the idea again and again of killing off the medical school because it either didn't work or cost too much. In fact, only in recent years have entire legislative sessions opened and closed without someone suggesting the medical school be closed — even after decades of superlative results.

As was required in this particular case, a hearing was held on the bill, but two things took place before the Fargo legislator could say word one. First, Earl Strinden, who was by now the majority leader in the House of Representatives, arranged to have the bill sent to a committee chaired by Brynhild Haugland.

If that wasn't enough of a stacked deck, consider what that Fargo man saw when he entered the hearing room. There was Dr.

Johnson, the medical school dean, about to take a seat toward the back of the room.

"Oh, Tommy," said Brynhild Haugland, pointing to the front row, "wouldn't you like to sit down here?"

As Vern Wagner recalls it, the Fargo man later said to him, "When I heard her say 'Oh, Tommy' I knew I was done for."

So it was that in 1981, ten years after he was named president, Clifford got what he wanted, a four-year, degree-granting medical school operating completely within North Dakota.

But even though those first 2-1-1 students got the short end of the thermometer, most people connected with the medical school back then have no regrets, and even believe it was best that UND didn't have to start that third year right away.

"We didn't really feel we were sophisticated enough in the medical community to take on the third and fourth year right away," says Keith Foster. "The 2-1-1 was a good plan because it introduced our docs here to medical education."

Foster, like the three other AHEC deans, was also learning on-the-job how to run a mini-medical school. He lined up the doctors to do the teaching of the returning fourth year students, recruited a chairman of each division and arranged for ongoing lectures and day-to-day exposure of the students to patients.

"Our physicians became more and more sophisticated," he says. "But when we started, to be honest, we didn't have the smarts to teach. By the time five years had elapsed, the work they had done with the returning fourth-year students had increased their sophistication and they had become excellent teachers."

During the transition from a two- to four-year school, John Vennes was asked by Clifford to serve as the acting dean of the School of Medicine. Ted Harwood had retired back to Vermont following the 1973 vote. He died not long after.

Vennes, whose Ph.D. was in microbiology could have become the permanent dean if he'd wanted. Clifford pressed him to take the job,

196

but he declined. He knew that without a medical degree, his standing would always be suspect to some element. Besides, he says, the school's national reputation really required that a medical doctor be at the helm. Vennes remained, however, as an associate dean and his value to the university was eventually recognized when on separate occasions he was awarded an Honorary Degree, the President's Medal and the prestigious Sioux Award.

As for Gary Dunn, "he was too valuable a person to let go," says Eelkema. He stayed on at the medical school, becoming a confidante of Clifford. When Tom Johnson became dean, he made Dunn an associate dean. Dunn played a key role in planning and building a Medical Education Building in Fargo adjacent to the Veterans Administration Hospital. While it wasn't quite a university teaching hospital, it was the next best thing, and remains today as one of the most important institutions in the curriculum.

Dunn continued to help in the recruiting process, even assisting some of the people he hired in finding homes. But he also borrowed money from some of them and they didn't get paid back, and that caused a good bit of friction.

In the early 1980s, Dunn developed brain cancer and couldn't function. In the four months before he died he had to undergo coronary bypass surgery. "He lived everybody's nightmare," says Eelkema.

Clifford remembers the last time he spoke to his lovable fraud. It was the same week that Clifford's wife, Florence had succumbed to cancer. Nancy Dunn phoned him and said Gary wanted to speak to him. No sooner had Dunn come on the phone, however, than he dropped the receiver and collapsed. Nancy picked up the phone a moment later and Clifford heard the words "Gary just died."

At his wake, Clifford followed an old Irish tradition, arriving with a ham under his arm. Eelkema leaned over Dunn's open casket and tucked a book into the pocket of his suit. Its title, "My $50,000 Year at the Races," by Andrew Beyer.

Dunn's death meant that all of the schemes he'd had floating in thin air collapsed around Nancy, his widow. She struggled for years to pay off old debts, remaining at UND as an administrator of the AHEC grant. Though she remained the same cheerful and energetic person she'd been when Gary was alive, there was an element of bitterness. Only recently, during an interview in Seattle where she now lives and has created a new life for herself, was she able to reveal the depth of that anger at Gary for leaving her with so many loose ends. After his wake and funeral, Dunn was cremated. Nancy went to the crematorium one day to claim the ashes. She carried them home in her car, placing the urn beneath the driver's seat. They remained there for ten years. Only when she sold the car did she decide Gary had finally earned her forgiveness. His ashes now rest in a cemetery near the Seattle airport.

In 2005, the School of Medicine at the University of North Dakota will celebrate its 100th birthday. In its infancy as a two-year program, it was recognized by the Carnegie Commission as one of the better schools in the country. A century later, it's a fully accredited medical school that serves as a model for others.

"The accreditation process is a pretty stern business," says Bill Harlan. "You can't fudge that. I've known enough places that have had accreditation troubles that you wouldn't think would, and they've had trouble getting it right. The system does not allow second-class performance or poor performance."

Today the School of Medicine and Health Sciences offers residency training in internal medicine, psychiatry, surgery and family medicine. In fact, within a year of the Legislature's adopting of the bill that started the 2-1-1 program, it began funding those residency programs.

Meanwhile, the hopes of all those legislators that more doctors would settle in North Dakota if the state had its own degree-granting school with residency training seem to have paid off.

"I think about fifty per cent of doctors now practicing in North

Dakota went to UND," says Dr. Jim Brosseau, Eelkema's successor as chair of the department of community medicine. "If we didn't have the medical school, I'm almost certain we wouldn't have as many doctors in North Dakota."

Brosseau, one of Grand Fork's busiest internists, still makes time to teach.

"We've got second-year students who come and spend seventy-eight hours with me in my practice," he says. "We make rounds on Saturday mornings and meet patients. One patient was scheduled for coronary bypass on Monday. So we went and found the surgeon who was doing the operation. The surgeon allowed the student to go into surgery with him to watch the bypass. Now he's coming to see the patient in post-op. The doctors love it when they have students. It's incredible how accessible they are as opposed to doctors in large university hospitals."

That exceptional nature of the UND School of Medicine, with students training alongside every-day doctors, is being copied more and more. The University of Minnesota, for example, uses community facilities for training because it works, says Brosseau. "That's where you find the people who are interested in teaching.

Graduates of the UND School of Medicine hold faculty positions in top schools across the country, including dozens of our graduates on the faculty of the University of Minnesota and the Mayo Clinic."

They have proven to be a very loyal group of alumni. Brosseau would know since he is a past president of the Alumni Association and knows most of them. "No school this size in the country — no public institution — has the kind of endowment we have," he says with pride.

Clifford can attest to that. During the centennial celebration of his hometown, Langdon, a few years ago, he was invited up to serve as grand marshal of the parade. An elderly woman approached him and he recognized her immediately. She was one of the Elliott girls, a pair of spinster sisters who taught music and were known for their frugal ways.

And their two cats. One of which had bitten the dust a long time back when a younger Clifford had drawn a bead on it from his upstairs window. He cringed as the woman drew near.

"Well, Tommy Clifford," she said, "you were a terror, but you turned out all right. I'm going to leave you some money at the university."

And she did: $575,000 for a music library.

"When Earl Strinden — who was executive director of the UND Alumni Association — when he heard that he said, 'God, Tom, you suppose you could go out and shoot a couple more cats?'"

Although it's easy now to see the School of Medicine as a success, not everyone was willing to admit that in the early days and years, says Brosseau.

"I think it was a gradual realization when our students were held up to national standards. How did they do on their national boards. How did they do on getting placement in their training. How successful were they once they got through school. We found that our students scored very well on those tests, they were well accepted by other programs, and once they got into practice they did very well. Once it was clear we were turning out a quality product, then everyone was on board."

But it wasn't just test scores that persuaded people, says Grandon Tolstedt.

"The thing that happened — these students, after they finished school and their residency training and started practicing in the state, they were the ones who started saying to other people, 'Hey, we've got a good school.' It took a while for some docs and some people to accept it. But what made it acceptable was that these students took hold and their treatment of people was accepted. They did a good job. All of a sudden people in the state were proud of the medical school. Because what happened, the older doctors retired. The ones who had been objecting to it weren't there after a while."

And even the objectors who are still there have changed their minds. Including the man who was perceived by some as the archenemy of the medical school, C. Warner Litten. Now retired and still living in Fargo, the affable Litten readily admits he was wrong those many years ago. In fact, he beams with pride at mention of the School of Medicine.

"I think history will record that it was a very wise decision," he says. "The whole tone of medicine in North Dakota is at a very high level and I think the medical school deserves a lot of credit for it. They've got a good school up there, there's no question about it."

PART TWO

Good Medicine

Out
on the
Tundra

21

Mark Olson is going fishing today.

And no one is going to stop him.

Dressed in green scrubs and white sneakers, he moves quickly across the parking lot of Mercy Hospital in Williston, toward his morning rounds. The sky this September morning is a sharp, flinty gray. For anyone else it's jacket weather. But Olson, a bear of a man with short blonde hair, a frothy blond beard and an easy smile, has no time for the cold.

"How's it goin', Doc?" calls a familiar face just inside the hospital lobby. The doctor waves, flashes a smile, but does not slow his purposeful movement.

"Goin' fishin'."

A quick check on the overnight admitting sheet tells him there are four patients to see this morning. You never know. They still call Williston "The Western Star," but it isn't the thriving place it was when Mark Olson grew up here in the 1970s, the son of a doctor in an oil boom town. Oil has pretty much gone bust, and if you drive around town these days you see too many old buildings closed up or converted into something other than for their original purpose.

There isn't as much activity any more, not as many young people. During the height of the boom, Olson's father was delivering 120 babies a year by himself. There are probably 100 to 200 born a year now, total. At Olson's recent twentieth high school reunion, four out of five class members had long since moved away. In the outlying regions, people are scarce enough that the word *rural* just won't cut it anymore. According to the federal government's population density formulas, it's officially a frontier. Still, for seventy miles in any direction, Mercy Hospital in Williston is the place you come to when you're sick.

The hospital corridors are quiet this morning as Mark Olson heads for his first patient. A quick stop at the nursing station to borrow a stethoscope and then he's in the intensive care unit. From outside the room one can hear him telling his elderly patient, "I'm going fishing but my assistant will .... "

Theresa, the ICU nurse who lent him her stethoscope, offers a whispered critique.

"He's the doctor all the staff go to," she says. "Even though insurance pays us to go to anyone, everyone goes to him. You can always tell a good doc. Who does the staff go to?"

At the bedside of his patient, Dr. Olson is chuckling. "Yes, I'm escaping," he says.

"I've got my boat all packed. My wife just can't understand why I'd want to go without her."

But his wife, Cindy, wouldn't dream of cramping his style. After the terrible flood of 1997 hit Grand Forks, where she and her husband and their two kids had lived since Mark finished medical school at UND, they decided to move back to his hometown of Williston. And they made a deal. Mark could still go fishing every now and then with his friends back in Grand Forks and Minnesota if he could get away from his busy practice. So far he'd postponed this trip twice.

Actually, the decision to move back to Williston more than made sense. At the time, Mark's father still practiced medicine here and they were able to work side by side for a year until his dad retired. Mark had left home at eighteen to go to college at UND, just as his father had done. In his father's day, however, UND's School of Medicine was a two-year affair, meaning he'd had to transfer in his third year. Transferring to another state always made it less likely that a hometown boy would come back after he got his medical degree. In the senior Olson's case, once he got his degree in Dallas and his residency training in Seattle, he was drafted into the Army. Still, when his service was completed, he came right back to Williston — and brought with him a six-year-old son named Mark.

"And I'm here now because I came home," says Mark, moving quietly along the Mercy Hospital corridor. "It's as simple as that. You set your priorities. What do you want in a new place? At the top of my list is family."

By the time he sees his next patient, a bricklayer in for a hip replacement and silicon-lung therapy. Dr. Olson has found his own stethoscope. He tells the man he'll arrange for someone to "snap a picture" of his lung. Because he himself is "skipping town."

"You docs … ," says the patient, rolling his eyes.

"Yeah," grins Olson, "I wouldn't want to work too much." On his way out, he calls over his shoulder, "Be sure to smile when they snap that picture. It's very important."

Working too much is an occupational hazard for any rural doctor. If he wanted to, Olson could put in a sixteen- or twenty-hour day and never slow down, never think about fishing. Small though his hometown might be, the need for a doctor never stops. If his schedule makes life challenging and hectic at the same time, it makes getaway trips with old buddies that much sweeter.

But wouldn't it be just as sweet to live out there where the fish were always biting?

Been there, done that, is his answer.

"Growing up here was good," he adds. "I had no complaints. The only reason I left was for education. They're hardworking people here. They value service. Whether it's someone who does good work for them on the farm or in a doctor's office. They appreciate someone who's working hard for them. They understand there's a value to that. There isn't the feeling that they're just entitled to it. They understand that things worth having are worth working for."

He pauses to smile. "If we went to Wal-Mart now, I wouldn't get past the checkout without running into six people I know. 'Hi, Doc, how you doin'.' People are friendly, personable. I would be surprised if you had a flat tire and pulled over to the side of the road that it would take more than three cars going by before someone stopped to help. I would be surprised."

That attitude of people helping people played a major role in his career decision as a young man.

"My dad didn't preach for me to go into medicine when I was growing up," he says. "He was careful to let me make my own decisions. He preached more by example, to find something that you enjoy, that you want to do everyday. I remember my dad going to work happy and coming home happy. I just don't ever remember thinking I was going to do anything else."

And there was no place he wanted to go to but the School of Medicine at UND. Unlike his father, Mark had the benefit of spending all four years, plus his residency training, in North Dakota. He did that training under the unique system at UND, working side-by-side with practicing community doctors.

In the days of the 1970s, before the medical school expanded, there was a huge concern that North Dakota didn't have enough population to produce the kinds of medical cases students would need to practice on. Never been a problem, he says.

"There were plenty of patients to get exposed to, to learn what you needed to learn in medical school," he says. "For general medical school exposure to pathology, what you need to get in medical school was more than adequate where I went. I don't think I was lacking at all. And one of the best things about a smaller program like UND's was the one-on-one time with the physicians. During my eight weeks of OB training, I worked with an obstetrician. For the whole eight weeks it was me and him. I did a month of surgery training out here in Williston and again it was just me and the surgeon. That's better than anything I would have gotten with any larger institution."

Since he's moved back to Williston, Olson has found lots of his fellow alumni from medical school both at the clinic he works for — Trinity Community Clinic, a not-for-profit clinic run by Trinity Health out of Minot — and at Mercy Health.

"Half of us at Trinity either had medical school or a residency at UND. Mercy has about six UND-educated doctors. In fact, about half the docs in the state went through UND. Would they have come back here to practice if they'd gone to medical school out of state? I don't think so. I think if you get educated here, the more likely you are to stay here. Look at Wyoming and Montana. They don't have a medical school. They don't have people coming back after they leave for med school. They stay gone."

A few years ago, Trinity Health bought out the clinic Olson's father had worked at for years. Mark now has his father's old office. He even has the same nurse his father had for years.

"I also have a lot of patients I inherited from my father. They come to me because they went to Dad. A lot of them reason that maybe I'll be okay, too. The elderly people here are impressed, happy that I came home."

But while the family medicine he practices is much the same as his father's, Olson is constantly reminded of the frontier status of his work. Williston is not Grand Forks. For instance, there are only a handful of specialists in Williston — general surgery, urology, neurology, obstetrics. There are cardiologists, gastroenterologists and psychiatrists who come over regularly from Minot or up from Bismarck. An oncologist comes up from Billings, Montana. This shortage often creates logistical problems. An example: there's only one OB/GYN doctor in Williston. The College of Obstetrics and Gynecology recommends that if you perform a V-back delivery — a vaginal birth after Caesarean — there should be immediate access to the physician and the surgical team. That means the doctor has to be in-house while the woman is in labor.

"He can't be at home," says Olson. "He can't be at his office. When you're the only guy in town, that's hard to do. It's hard for Williston to offer that service. And problems are the exception not the rule. Nineteen out of twenty V-backs go without a hitch. Probably more."

The option, he says, is for a doctor to perform a standard C-section, not a V-back. Or to have the expectant mother move to Bismarck or Minot when she gets close to delivery time.

"Another thing: we don't do cardiology here. But we can get people to a cardiologist in a couple of hours — assuming it's not a January blizzard. I guess it's as much as you can ask living in frontier America. Patients understand that if you live in Williston and you come to the emergency room with a heart attack, you're not going to see a cardiologist. You're gonna see me and if it's something I'm not comfortable taking care of, you're going to be on the road quickly to see the cardiologist."

The patients he does see tend to be more elderly than in Grand Forks.

"The patients I see are probably more complicated than what I would see in Grand Forks. There are two internists in town. They're too busy to take all the complicated patients, so we end up with a lot of them.

"The biggest difference in my little world is access to specialists.

In Grand Forks you could walk down the hall and get advice, let's say, from a dermatologist. You didn't have to send them 220 miles away to see a dermatologist. It took some getting used to, making the decision here to call an ambulance at 2 A.M. to take someone to Minot, versus if the cardiologist could come down the hall to see them. You're constantly learning here. Because you know it's going to be three days out of someone's life to drive to Bismarck and back, so you want to try to help them. You stay a little bit more on top of your game. You have to be better read, you're using textbooks more than just saying it's a problem for a dermatologist. It's more challenging and I like that."

The other side of that coin is one of the most valuable lessons he learned at UND.

"The best family physicians, I feel, are very comfortable with what they don't know. You get yourself in trouble if you don't know what you don't know. You can't know everything. You have to be able to say, 'I don't know. I need help.' If you're not comfortable saying that, if you need to know everything, then you need to sub-specialize so you can know all there is to know about a smaller piece of the puzzle. I like to think I know what I don't know. If I need help, if I'm seeing something I'm uncomfortable with, I don't have any problem telling people we need to send you to see so-and-so to get you help."

He's seen his last patient, he's scribbling a last-minute note on a chart at a nurse's station. Over the public address system comes a soothing religious message about ways to "establish channels of good will ...." The nurse at the station is grumping about being overworked. Olson smiles. "We'd complain if our life was boring, too."

Easy for him to say. He's going fishing. Heading for the front door of the hospital, that's all he is talking about. He's saying it will take him a full day to drive up to Minnesota and then a full a day to drive back. Which brings up an important rule, he says. "If it takes two days to drive to a fishing vacation, you have to have three days of fishing."

He's not talking about the walleye you can catch on Lake Sakakawea just down the road. He enjoys that, but what he loves most of all are the bass he'll be fishing for with his buddies over in Bemidji.

"I love 'em. They put up a fight and they are so stupid. You can catch the same fish over and over. They're big and stupid."

He turns the corner in the hallway. The front door to the hospital is now in sight. But between him and the door sits a man with several brochures and pamphlets laid out neatly on a card table. He is a drug rep from Bismarck. Olson's shoulders sag. He spends ten minutes listening politely as the rep talks about a new drug coming on the market.

Olson asks, "How about side effects? I don't want to end up getting phone calls ...."

When he finally breaks free, he says that his mentor while at UND medical school was Dr. Casey Ryan, an internist. "I'll never forget what he said. He told me you can't know all the drugs. So you get comfortable with certain drugs. But he also said if you can't name the three most common side effects of a drug, you have no business prescribing it."

He is five feet from the hospital entrance when a woman approaches him. You didn't forget about the picture, did you? Staff photos are being taken this afternoon.

Either he did forget or he's faking it. It looks like he's faking it. In fact, it looks like he's blowing it off.

"I'm not delaying my fishing trip to get my picture taken," he says, breaking free. "I'm outa here."

And he very nearly makes it. He's crossing the parking lot to his white SUV when someone calls out, "Mark." He stops, looks around. A man he recognizes as the relative of a patient approaches. They start to talk. Curiously, there is none of the anxiety about breaking away as there was when the drug rep cornered him. Olson spends ten minutes talking to the man about his concerns for his relative. Then he shakes his hand, smiles and moves on.

"Williston," he says, "is a long ways from everywhere. It's got an airport and you can get places — the connections are poor, but you can get places. Things move slower here on the Tundra. But I'm gonna stay here. People are nice to me here."

And then he's gone.

Gone fishin'.

Therein Starts Life's Journey

22

It's almost impossible to go more than twenty feet in North Dakota without running into someone named Johnson. In the medical community, it's more like ten. And among doctors in the state, the name Johnson almost automatically brings up the little town of Rugby, so much a part of mainstream small-town America that it is, in fact, the geographical center of the North American continent. There's a monument there to prove it.

There are also a lot of doctors named Johnson, going back to the time in the early twentieth century when citizens of Rugby got their care from the Johnson Clinic. The core of the Rugby Johnsons was five young boys, immigrants from Iceland who arrived in North Dakota as youngsters with nothing but the clothes on their backs. Each of them contracted tuberculosis as children, but each regained his health, thanks to a mother who drove them to thrive and succeed. Two of the brothers went on to became doctors of note, founding the Rugby clinic and earning reputations for their

215

diagnosis and treatment. One other brother had to settle for being attorney general and later a state Supreme Court justice.

That would be the father of Dr. George Magnus Johnson, the compact, gray-haired dynamo moving quickly along the street in Fargo on this morning, heading for the Merit Care Hospital. Today, as usual, he's parked blocks from the hospital — for exercise — and is carrying a well-worn leather backpack. Dapper is the right word to describe him: a blue sports coat, a yellow shirt with pale blue checks, a red tie, tan slacks. His red stethoscope is slung round his neck as are his reading glasses.

Walking, talking, Dr. Johnson seems always to have a ready story about one of the Johnson men in his family — a cousin or an uncle. In all, including himself, seven Johnsons have become doctors. To a man, he is saying as he crosses the street to the hospital, each has been a loyal supporter down the years of the idea of a medical school in North Dakota. For without it, the Johnson boys might have had to become lawyers. Even his own father, says Dr. George Johnson fondly, told him he should become a doctor — that's how much he admired his brothers' achievements.

"They were poor immigrant boys who went to medical school here because there was no other choice," he is saying. "We didn't have enough money to go anywhere else. My lifelong best friend, who is my wife's cousin, was a farm boy from northeastern North Dakota, also the son of Icelandic immigrants. He came to UND wearing a pair of orange corduroys. They were the only pair of pants he had. He didn't have the requisite high school courses to go to a big university. So he had to take high school courses in Grand Forks for three months. I roomed with him for many years. He worked in the Student Union at night making pies. He became a very successful radiologist."

Entering the hospital through the Roger Maris Cancer Center, Johnson recalls playing basketball against Maris as a teen. How Maris knocked him down.

216

"I realized then how strong he was." Breezing past the bank of elevators, he enters a stairwell and sets a blistering pace up four flights to the David W. Todd Conference Room named after a popular doctor who has recently died. "I look forward to climbing those stairs every week," says Johnson, showing no sign of labored breathing or perspiration.

As he enters the room, he reflects, "As a doctor, when you don't have access to medical education, you don't become as striving or as astute at self-educating as you should be. Education of students is the best route to your own self-education. Every time I meet with a new group of students, I say I'm not here to teach you. You will learn and I will learn with you."

Inside the Todd room, seated around a conference table with expectant eyes, are the reasons he has come here today. Since 1970, Johnson has been a practicing pediatrician and faculty member at the UND School of Medicine. For fifteen of those years he was chairman of the department of pediatrics, widely known for his work in pediatric diabetes and epidemiology. Though retired from the chairman's job, he can't stop teaching.

At the table sits Candalaria Feliz, studying pediatric medicine as a third year medical student in the ROME program (Rural Opportunities in Medical Education). Next to her is Jannelle Jones, also in the middle of her pediatric rotation. She's also a member of the state National Guard and frequently comes to medical school still in uniform from her Guard duties.

Johnson relishes his twice-weekly sessions with students like these. Today he's here to review cases and lead the students on rounds in the pediatric wing. He likes to begin by throwing out real-life case histories, holding back critical details to see how his students respond. That's what medical school is all about he says. "Each case triggers a different story. Thus, you need lots of cases."

He begins by describing the case of a woman who complained of a runny nose before contracting meningitis. But her doctors missed the diagnosis. Without telling the students about the meningitis, Johnson asks what they would do.

"Is it mucousy?

"No. It's a clear drip."

"Could it be spinal fluid coming through?"

He's smiling now. These kids are sharp.

"What test would you run?"

"Glucose?" asks Candalaria.

Johnson beams. It's the right answer, of course, and he quickly fills them in on the details of the case.

"If they'd checked for glucose, they perhaps could have prevented meningitis," he says. Because they'd missed it, the woman became ill and sued for malpractice in a celebrated case.

"As to why she didn't develop the drip from her nose until she was in her fifties?" Johnson lets the question hang. "Cerebrospinal fluid drip through a sinus defect: this is a pearl, if you will."

Johnson keeps a list with him that he adds to each day and puts in his shirt pocket. It will contain eight or nine disparate things — a student question he needs to ponder, something he's forgotten and wants to be sure to look up. He sees it as his way to keep educating himself, and he encourages his students to have their lists as well.

"We can't teach you all of pediatrics here," he will say. "We can show you what pediatrics is and isn't and give you an outline in terms of what to look for on your national exam. But you'll have to learn pediatrics by experience, through cases and other ways through all of your career."

"That's always been my approach," says Johnson. "I feel it's the only effective approach in a medical school. Then the students aren't threatened, like I was constantly threatened in medical school. This big ego stuff is one of the worst things in medicine."

The threats never came at the University of North Dakota in the 1950s when he attended the old two-year medical school. Far from it. At UND he says, he found only nurturing.

But he transferred in his third year to the big city medical school at the University of Washington in Seattle.

"That was a big disappointment, to be honest. It was then a totally different place than here. Perhaps here at North Dakota we were nurtured too much, in a way. But UW didn't pay any attention to us transfer students. The school was not student-oriented. At that time, the medical school had what they called 'terror services.' The idea was that in educating young people in medicine, you needed to frighten them into studying and working hard. There were any number of professors at UW who believed in this terror services aspect. Being from a family that highly valued independence — as many people of Icelandic origin are — I chafed. I almost quit medical school. I stayed because I knew that the way my uncles practiced medicine in that country setting of Rugby was the right way of medical practice."

Though he met his wife in Seattle, Johnson hurried back to the Midwest in the mid 1960s to a place where he felt he belonged. "At UW, their interest in students seemed last and least. At the time of my graduation, I received very discouraging comments from an advisor who didn't know me. I've kept it in mind throughout all my years in dealing with medical students. As they form themselves, they have many uncertainties — even the oldest and brashest of them — and they need the right word of support at the right time. I've tried to pride myself on doing so based on the lack of it in my own experience."

In the Todd room, Johnson begins working through a list of the patients who will be seen on today's rotation. First is a young man with a kidney stone, something you'd expect to find only in an adult.

"That's rare," he says. "I've never seen a kidney stone in the first decade of life. What's the most common reason for a stone in pediatrics?"

"Maybe he can't process calcium?"

"Very good," he smiles. "Hypercalcuria. I myself had a stone when

I was in my twenties. The second most common cause of blood in the urine is hypercalcuria ...."

It was also during his twenties that Johnson experienced what he likes to call his "marvelous medical adventure." Between UW and his return to North Dakota, Johnson spent time working at the Centers for Disease Control and Prevention in Atlanta. He became an investigator for the fledgling Epidemic Intelligence Service (EIS). Before his stint was done, Johnson became one of very few doctors in the United States to have a disease named after him. Sort of. Actually, he's extremely circumspect about mentioning it; even his own family doesn't use his name when referring to the Reye-Johnson syndrome.

In 1963, an Australian pathologist named R. Douglas Reye, M.D., published findings about a previously unknown fatal disease he had come across in New South Wales. It killed dozens of children who had been suffering from the flu or a viral infection such as the chickenpox. Autopsies showed their brains and livers were badly swollen. The disease quickly became known as Reye's syndrome, and the Centers for Disease Control in Atlanta later went on to blame the disease on the use of aspirin.

But a year before Dr. Reye's article was published, George Johnson had written about a deadly outbreak he'd come across as an investigator with the EIS. In several small North Carolina towns, he examined the cases of sixteen teens who had died in a four-month period of something that resembled encephalitis. It happened during a flu epidemic. Johnson submitted his findings on this previously unknown syndrome to the American Journal of Diseases in Children. But the hidebound editors sent his article back, saying he should have known the piece needed to go to an epidemiological journal.

In fact, the young Johnson didn't know. He had never written a paper for publication before and wasn't doing so now to jump into the research-publishing-fame-game. He assumed only that his findings might be interesting to other doctors who had been puzzled over similar deaths.

"I remember a pathologist in Greensboro, North Carolina, saying to me, 'But I have examined two little kids, and both have died of brain swelling. Young man, we'd better sit down and write up a couple of these cases because I think they're important."

Johnson still has the rejection letter from what was then the AMA *Journal of Disease of Children.* By the time he found a journal interested, Dr. Reye had already published his own independent theories on the syndrome and his name was forever attached to it. For years, Dr. Johnson served on the board of National Reye's Syndrome Foundation, and gave keynote addresses at several of their convocations. And among a small group of researchers and epidemiologists, the disease is referred to as the Reye-Johnson syndrome — at which Johnson can only smile ruefully. In truth, he's much more upset that the CDC would blame the disease solely on the use of aspirin — something that Johnson doesn't believe.

"I don't think it's common sense to believe that teens don't take aspirin once in a while when they have the flu. But because of the warnings CDC has put on this, aspirin is usually prohibited. But none of the people at CDC are clinicians."

His experience at EIS sparked a lifelong fascination with the course of disease. "The reason, perhaps, for the decrease in the Reye's syndrome over the years is the same reason swine influenza disappeared," he says. "Things change in influenza ecology and that changes the incidence of disease. If there's anything that's impressive, it's how disease rates change over time.

"Certainly swine influenza came and went. It killed my father's brother in 1918. It killed healthy, young, strong people. It didn't kill many with chronic disease or debility. To this day the reasons for that are totally unknown. And this is one of the great secrets of infectious disease in the past century. Likewise, Reye's syndrome came and went. And whether that disease comet will ever come back again is unknown."

Next on the list of patients is an eleven-month-old child suffering from a viral illness, but also from ITP, a disorder associated with bleeding. The child has few bruises, but she has suffered a nosebleed. Her platelet count is very low. She is now stabilized.

"What's the worst thing that could have happened?" asks Johnson. "It's rare but you should know it."

Again, Janelle: "An intra-cranial bruise?"

"Yes," says Johnson. "She could have bumped her head. What if she became unconscious? At the door of the emergency room, what would you do next? Where is the source of pathology in ITP?"

"The platelets," says Janelle. "The spleen is chewing them up." Johnson is nodding.

"Like a combine chews up corn during harvest. So what would you set up right now so she doesn't die?"

When they are slow to answer, he says softly, "I recall two cases of this rare situation. The patients died. I never forgot about those deaths."

"Give them platelets?"

"Why do that?" he challenges. "They'll be destroyed as soon as you give them."

Still no answer around the table.

"You go to surgery right now," he says looking his students in the eyes, "and you take out the spleen. Bing! Right now!"

"But the spleen ...?"

"The spleen shouldn't come out unless there's a good reason," says Johnson, nodding. "But this is obviously a good reason."

Sometimes, Johnson admits, he comes across as a little dogmatic. If he does, he's one of the more gentle dogmatists in medicine. But one thing he's emphatic about is the point in his life when he changed from someone with a general interest in medicine to someone driven by a mission. In 1969, within five months of each other, his two young sons, aged seven and two, were diagnosed with Type 1 insulin-dependent diabetes.

Until that time he had little idea or interest in diabetes. Suddenly, he knew, he had to become an expert.

Among the things he soon found out was that North Dakota, for some mysterious reason, has the highest incidence of child and adolescent diabetes. Getting up to speed on diabetes, he says now, was a means of mental stability and personal survival for himself and his family. "Although my wife handled it better than I did. So finding a treatment for child diabetes has been my prayer. And I still see children with diabetes all over the state." Today, because of Johnson's quest, North Dakota has become known as a state with several solid programs serving children and adolescents with diabetes.

The news of his sons' diabetes caused Johnson to rethink his entire medical career. He and his family were living in Bismarck at the time, where there weren't more than a handful of pediatricians. But in Fargo he found a critical mass of advanced thought and practice in pediatric diabetes.

"I just decided I had to find out all I could," he says. "I was thunderstruck psychologically. The prognosis for diabetes at that time was very poor. Death was said to occur in the twenties, which subsequently proved to be wrong over wrong."

At the time in North Dakota there was an old doctor in Grand Forks named Edgar Haunz, who had started the second diabetes camp for children in the United States., in North Dakota right after World War II. Johnson and Haunz soon became friends.

"He was a flamboyant and bluff character," says Johnson. "He wore a bow tie, a three-piece suit, a big gold chain, played the cello. He always had a cigar in his mouth. Drove a huge, long Cadillac. Even though he was an internist, he still did this diabetes camp for kids. When I moved to Fargo, he was getting old. He said someone has to take over and I need to have you do this. So therein starts life's journey."

The daily rounds have begun. With Johnson in the lead, the group approaches the open door of a patient room. Johnson knocks gently on the door.

"May we invade?"

The patient is a teen-aged boy recovering from meningitis. He's doing well and Johnson chats with his parents. As he leaves, he fixes the teen with a fatherly look. "Be sure to wear your seat belt, okay? I always mention seat belts. That's because I'm a crabby old man."

Across the hall, the students push into the room of a woman whose newborn is jaundiced and is sleeping in an incubator. Taking some history from the woman, Johnson brightens. "You're breast feeding? Congratulations."

He shakes her hand and turns to his students.

"I firmly believe in breast-feeding," he says. "Only about half of mothers try to breast-feed and only half of those are successful. Lack of breast-feeding is associated with all kinds of decreased morbidity. But young women in America are not exposed to discussion of breast-feeding at the ages of twelve to fifteen, as they are in Europe."

He turns again to the woman, sitting on the edge of her bed. "Thank you very much. Your baby is lucky to have you as a mom."

Even though he moved to Fargo for the advanced medical expertise it offered, Johnson never quite became an establishment Fargo doctor. He got off on the wrong foot right away when he refused to wear a white coat.

"I was with little kids all day and the white coat was very off-putting to them," he says, "And to their families."

This was during the early 1970s when the university in Grand Forks was trying to convert the medical school from a two- to four-year, degree-granting institution. Johnson was stunned at the opposition to the idea from his Fargo colleagues.

"Some of the older physicians were trained at traditional medical schools like UW. They had that traditional training and they believed that you had to have a large university hospital to train medical students. Some of us felt very strongly about this school and what it did for young people in particular and what it did for the state and what it meant to the state."

Johnson worked hard to make sure the plan for a four-year school survived, hosting informational sessions led by his former professor and medical school dean at UND, Dr. John Vennes. He says he's spent his career trying to emulate the Vennes style.

"Always the teachers at this school have cared the most about their students, not their own status or salary," says Johnson. "It really exemplifies the comment one for all and all for one. Never once when I was chairman did I hear wrangling or argument about salaries or personal advancement. The discussion was uniformly how to benefit the students. That's the way it was when I was a student at UND."

"Anytime you can grab a kid and immunize him, do it," says Johnson in the corridor to his students. "One of the best places to immunize a child who needs more immunizations is while they're in the hospital." He tells a story about conning an Amish family into getting their child vaccinated. The mother had told him that pertussis — whooping cough — was supposed to happen to kids. She said her own mother had told her that.

"But I got one in," he said, smiling. "There is no indication for not giving a vaccine — unless the patient is immune suppressed. You can give vaccines and suffer no consequences. But use common sense. First you get a child's temperature down. If there is anything positive we do in pediatrics, it's giving vaccines. End of speech."

"The state is now better supplied with good physicians since the advent of the four-year school," he says, "The physicians across the state are better than they've ever been in all the years I've been here. Agriculture in this state is like a huge sea — the wave goes up and down and sometimes the trough gets deeper and deeper. But not so with this medical school. Everything is going better and better and better.

"It's hard to know what would have happened without the medical school," he says. "I compare our situation to Montana's. I know that our health care and delivery, even with all its faults, is sophisticated here. We've got three nationally approved diabetes centers here. I think without the medical school, the state would be quite bereft medically."

Since 1970, Johnson has seen between 500 and 600 families with child and adolescent diabetes — in addition to doing general pediatrics and teaching at the medical school. Although he has stepped down as chairman of the department of pediatrics, he has continued as a faculty member and leads medical students on pediatric rounds at the Merit Care hospital in Fargo twice a week. He still drives up to Grand Forks once a week to the Altru clinic to see child and adolescent diabetes patients, and spends three days a month in Bismarck doing the same.

"The happiest time of my entire life was between 1986 to 2001 when I was the chairman with those students," he says. "I was busy morning noon and night. I gave up hunting and all my hobbies, because I enjoyed those students so much. And I'm having a little trouble now getting toward retirement. A little personal trouble shifting that gear on the old pickup."

They are discussing the case of a 14-month-old child who was rushed from a day-care nursery to the emergency room after a fit of choking and wheezing. Doctors did a check for a foreign body in the throat. Nothing was found, but there was an irritation in his airway. As it turns out, Candaleria reports, the day-care provider had given the child a hot dog.

"Wrong over wrong over wrong," Johnson groans. "Who is the lowest person on the health-care totem pole in status and salary? It's day-care workers. They should know a hot dog is the most dangerous food you can give a fourteen-month-old. It's full of gristle. It'll hang up in their throats. Another absolute of pediatric medicine: a kid who suddenly wheezes, from ten months to two-and-a-half years —

it's always a foreign body until ruled otherwise. And when a child coughs up a foreign body, whether nuts, sunflower seeds, a hot dog — all of them are dangerous. Just a word or two from you in anticipatory guidance could prevent a death. So the key point: always mention it to parents."

Moments later, he is taking the steps two at a time on his way to the ground floor. He has as much energy as a twenty-year old. He turns and grins. "Oh, they'll make fine physicians."

Lewis and Clark and Mayer

23

The legend of the Snake Woman got started on a warm summer evening three years ago in the small town of Mandaree, on the Fort Berthold Indian Reservation in northwestern North Dakota. As her father worked nearby trimming weeds with a swather, a six-year-old girl played on the grass in front of her house. Minutes later, her teenage sister saw the little girl suddenly favoring her hand. She had Down syndrome and couldn't talk to tell her older sister what was wrong. When their father took a look, he noticed the swelling. Somehow, he thought, she'd broken her hand.

The girl's father knew that as a member of the Three Affiliated Tribes — the Mandan, Hidatsa and Arikara — who live on the Fort Berthold Reservation, he was entitled to free medical care through the federally funded Indian Health Service. But instead, as he gathered his daughter and rushed to his car, he was thinking about an all-star, all-state basketball player he'd gone to high school with years ago, right here on the reservation.

She was a doctor now, practicing in a private clinic up in New

Town, about thirty miles away. Her name was Monica Mayer, the strong-willed, dark-eyed offspring of a German farmer and a Native American woman of the Three Tribes. That's where the father and his daughter headed that August night, not realizing that time was rapidly running out.

In New Town, the private clinic was closed. The area was just too small to support an all-night clinic. The father faced a decision. Turn around and head for the closer IHS office. Or drive another thirty miles to Stanley, where, according to a note at the New Town clinic, Dr. Mayer was working a shift in the small emergency room.

There was no question in his mind, for he remembered the Indian name Monica Mayer had been given later in life by her grandmothers: to everyone at Fort Berthold, she was "Good Medicine."

Two doctors worked the night shift in the emergency room at Stanley. One was a doctor from India, finishing up his three years at a rural health post so he could qualify for a green card and be on the path toward citizenship. But he didn't speak English well and seldom saw women or children. It meant that the other doctor, Monica Mayer, was almost always busy.

Shortly after 9 P.M. that night, the father from Mandaree came in with his daughter. Her hand, by now, was swollen to the wrist, the skin so taut it looked like a water balloon. Mayer did an immediate X-ray, which ruled out a broken bone. Then she played a hunch. She likes to joke that in medical school at the University of North Dakota, she might not always have gotten the highest test scores, but she was a darned good diagnostician.

"Have you seen any snakes in your yard?" she asked the father as she cleansed the little girl's hand.

No, he said, but a friend, old man Plenty Chief, had seen quite a few at his place nearby. To a doctor, a hunch is one thing, but nothing beats evidence. Mayer dipped the little girl's hand in water and pulled it out to see if there was any bubbling anywhere that would indicate a break in the skin. She took a magnifying glass and combed the hand, finding two small incisions between the fourth and fifth fingers.

Fang marks.

She stared at the girl's father and said, "She got bit by a damn rattlesnake."

Immediately she thought of what might have happened if, like many parents, this man had simply given the girl some aspirin for her hand and put her to bed, thinking it could wait until morning to see a doctor. This girl would never make it to morning.

As it was, there was only one thing that could save her. Anti-snake venom.

Mayer quickly called Trinity Hospital in Minot — another place she knew very well. For she'd spent most of her training as a University of North Dakota medical student in the family care program in Minot. Unlike the big medical schools in larger states, North Dakota put its medical students out in the communities in specially designed clinics. There the students work side-by-side with community doctors who double as faculty, imparting medical know-how while treating patients.

A year earlier, in 1999, Mayer had completed her residency training in Minot. She was snatched up quickly by Trinity and given the job she'd committed herself to years earlier: taking care of the health of people on her reservation.

On the phone to Trinity in Minot, she learned that the only anti-snake venom in the state was in Bismarck, and then only five vials. Mayer estimated the girl would need at least fifteen vials to save her life. Bismarck, the site of another UND medical school clinic, immediately shipped its five vials north, while Mayer sent her patient and father on to Minot to meet them. In the meantime, Trinity officials contacted Children's Hospital in Denver, which dispatched an airplane to Minot. It picked up the little girl and transfused ten more vials into her on the way back to Denver. It was life-and-death now. Snake venom goes after blood cells and causes massive internal bleeding. By the time the plane touched down in Colorado, the extremely aggressive venom had gotten as far as the little girl's heart.

But that's as far as it got.

Later, two doctors from Denver called Mayer to write an article about the case for a medical journal. How, they wanted to know, had she been able to diagnose the snakebite so quickly.

"I said you can't make a diagnosis like that without knowing the geographical location." The two doctors, who kept mispronouncing Minot as *Mee-know*, didn't understand. So she explained.

She'd known that her friend from high school lived on the western bank of the Missouri River. Born and raised on the reservation herself, the doctor known as "Good Medicine" knew that in August, on the western bank, rattlesnakes shed their skin. When they do that they are blinded and will strike at any movement without being able to give a rattle as a warning.

"I could almost picture what had happened," she recalls. "Snakes like to hide in tall grass or hay where it's cool. Meanwhile, there was this little girl out in the yard. Perhaps she saw the snake and reached down and it struck her. Like a normal little child, she knew she'd done something wrong. So she goes in the house to hide it and the older sister discovers it."

Ah, said the doctor from Denver, so you've done these before?

In fact, said Mayer, "I'd never seen a snakebite before. I'd only read about them. But I knew snakes lived on the west side of the Missouri."

Aside from that journal article, the snake story has opened a new chapter in Dr. Mayer's life. In Grand Forks, editors at the UND alumni magazine heard about the snake and came out to do a story. While puttering around Mayer's office, they discovered something unusual on her walls: lots of pictures of the famous explorers of 1803, Meriwether Lewis and William Clark.

Oh, that, she said. She'd been studying the Lewis and Clark history since she was twelve years old. In fact, a young girl who lived near her in New Town brought her a card that proves her life-long interest in the great American explorers who bonded so advantageously with the Mandan, Hidatsa and Arikara tribes. The little girl down the street had checked out an old book from the local school library. It was called *The Upper Missouri River Indians and Lewis and Clark*. It still had in the inside pocket a library card signed by the last student who'd read the book. The name on the card: Monica Mayer, 1972.

What interested the UND alumni writer was the angle Mayer had been applying to Lewis and Clark. She was fascinated by the medical aspects of their momentous journey from St. Louis, up through western North Dakota and on to the Pacific and back. At the slightest provocation she could rattle off innumerable facts about Lewis, Clark and early nineteenth century health care.

The next thing she knew, H. David Wilson, the dean at the School of Medicine at UND, had her on the phone. He invited her to deliver a talk on Lewis and Clark and medicine during the prestigious Dean's Hour on the Grand Forks campus. That talk triggered dozens of other invitations, and, lo only a short time out of medical school, Dr. Mayer had become Snake Woman, Rattlesnake Girl, and a nationally-recognized expert on Lewis and Clark.

The attention has been flattering and fun, she says, but the handle she still likes best is that of Good Medicine. For it's not just a fairly appropriate name, it's an identity that encompasses medicine and mission.

"Some people thought I probably didn't make an intelligent move as far as personal gain and fame and fortune," she says of her return to the small reservation town where she grew up. "But there is a method to my madness. I selected friends and family as my first priority."

Getting the priority straight, however, took some doing, although at first everything looked easy.

As a gifted athlete at New Town High School, Mayer was twice named to the All-State Girls B Basketball Team and made the All-Sportscasters/Writers State Team in 1976. She was even state bowling team champion four times. Her talent and hard work won her a basketball scholarship to UND-Minot.

"It was my ticket off the reservation, so to speak," she says. "I've always been very thankful for my talent for sports. But I worked hard at it, too. It's that commitment to hard work, a German attitude, that I got from my father."

Ervin Mayer's education, however, like that of most farm boys of his day, had ended at the eighth grade. Monica vividly recalls her father's relentless life as a laborer, whether it was spent hauling coal, riding horses on fence-fixing duty, shoveling grain or driving a truck. It was a hard life. She never quite appreciated how hard, until one particular Saturday morning when her eyes were opened.

"My two younger sisters and I weren't doing well in school," she says. "My father, whose family homesteaded here, worked from sunup to sundown every day. We weren't wealthy. We barely got by, but we were well cared for. I was in the eighth grade. One Saturday morning at 7 A.M., my father loaded all three of us up in his truck and dropped us off in one of the fields, fifteen miles away. He said, 'I want all these rocks picked and piled in those corners.' We had sandwiches and water. He said, 'I'll come back and pick you up at the end of the day. And I want it done.' So after we worked hard all day, and were sweaty and dirty and tired and sore, my dad drives up. I'm sure he wanted to laugh at us. I was the oldest, so I had a speech ready to give to him — how this wasn't fair, it wasn't right we had to work this hard.

"My dad looked at me and he said, 'By God, do you think I like to work this hard all day long? No. Your mother said you girls do not like school and you're not doing well in school. So we figured you might as well get ready for how life is going to be. If you don't want to get your education, this is how it's going to be. You will work sunup to sundown if you're going to make it in life. Unless, of course, you want to get better grades in school.'"

Her eyes got wide.

"I said, 'You mean all we have to do is get good grades in school and we won't have to come out here and work like this?' He says, 'That's right.'

"I always remember that story," she smiles. "One day of hard labor changed our whole life. My youngest sister, Hollie, went on and became valedictorian of New Town High."

And Monica went on, eventually, to UND-Minot to play basketball. But she hit a snag.

"I was not focused enough and had that sense of freedom as an eighteen-year-old," she says. "My first year I messed up. I tell kids today, 'You're gonna mess up. But you need to have some fun and get it out of your system before you settle down.' I left Minot because my parents told me I either needed to quit school and get a job and become a working person or start anew."

She started over at UND-Williston Junior College and did well. She even played basketball, with her team finishing seventh in the nation. It was enough to land her a basketball scholarship at Northern Arizona University in Flagstaff. But while there, a knee injury ended her playing career, along with her hopes of joining the first women's Olympic trials in 1980.

But she did graduate from Northern Arizona with a degree in education and settled into a life in Flagstaff as a schoolteacher. It was about that time that her grandmothers gave her the Hidatsa name that had been her great-grandmother's: Good Medicine. At the time, she says, "My image of myself was as a jockette. When I was teaching school, I was also coaching the girls' track and field teams. I found myself spending a lot of time with injured athletes. They had various dislocations and I learned how to rehabilitate them. It reminded me that when I was growing up, I'd put Popsicle sticks on the legs of cats. I thought I was going to be a veterinarian, until I realized you had to study all the different animals. And it just seemed easier to me to study the human body. It was just one body."

She says her mother had always hounded her daughters to consider a medical career. "She'd make us bring an apple to school on the day we got our shots to give to the nurse. She'd see the nurse and say, 'Look at that nurse. Oh, Lord, I pray one of you girls will be a nurse someday. They're so smart and pretty.' My sister Hollie fell for that scam. We always tease her about that. My mom's best friends were nurses. I told my dad once I might want to be a nurse or a doctor. And he said, 'Well, you know I don't like doctors. But you're always going to have sick people, so there will always be a job.'"

When her father died of a heart attack, she left her teaching job in Arizona. She and her sister loaded up their father's truck and moved to Grand Forks, where Hollie enrolled in pre-nursing and Monica in pre-med.

"It was a changing point for all of us in our family," she says. "His death, Hollie and Renee and me, we all went on."

In fact, all three of Avis Mayer's daughters graduated from UND and each is now back at Forth Berthold in health care. Hollie is a nurse with the Indian Health Service, and Renee has a master's degree in social work and works with foster children.

"My mother was insistent you get your education and come back home and share it with your people," says Mayer. "And that is kind of a trend here in North Dakota."

In a recent column in the *Grand Forks Herald*, Dorreen Yellow Bird wrote a story about Monica Mayer's career, recalling that when Monica's mother mentioned that her daughter wanted to go to medical school, Dorreen thought it would be impossible.

"I wondered how this young Hidatsa woman, in spite of the fact that she was exceptional, could become a medical doctor," wrote Yellow Bird. "There was none on the reservation at the time. Her father was deceased, and her mother worked as a secretary. There were few American Indian doctors nationwide."

But there *was* an innovative program at the University of North Dakota's School of Medicine, designed especially for someone of Mayer's background. For in 1972, at about the time she was reading her book on Lewis and Clark, Dr. Robert Eelkema was shaking the grant tree in Washington. Eelkema was chairman of the department of community medicine at the time, and he'd been searching for funds to help UND convert its two-year medical school into a four-year, degree-granting institution. He was well known in Grand Forks for his uncanny ability to sniff out the odd pile of unused federal dollars in Washington and to create, almost on the spot, a program that could make use of those funds.

He found his grant that guaranteed the expansion to a four-year medical school, but he also came up with an idea for helping Indians get medical training. He devised a program called "Indians into Medicine," shortened to the catchy title INMED. With it, UND had the money to pay for half a dozen Indian medical students each year. The program has been so successful that INMED now accounts for one of every four medical degrees granted to Indians in America.

This was the program that gave Monica Mayer her chance. She graduated from UND's School of Medicine, having been trained through the Minot Center for Family Medicine Residency Program. Like many new doctors, the brand-new Dr. Mayer didn't realize how well she'd been trained. "Because when you come out of medical school, you're scared of your own shadow. You think 'Oh my goodness, a heart attack is going to come into the emergency room and it's just me and a nurse.'"

She not only did fine, Trinity promoted her to run its New Town clinic. There she juggled her duties with trips every other day to Stanley to cover its failing emergency room. It was during that time that Mayer treated her first rattlesnake bite. That experience boosted her confidence, but she found the Stanley days to be draining.

"We were dying out there," she says. "It was just me and a doc from India. An internist who didn't do women and children. Stanley has an affiliation with Trinity but the hospital was looking pretty grim. In fact, it was going to close."

After observing the situation for several months, she finally approached the new administrator. She noted that, technically, all ambulances carrying patients from the area to Minot — the nearest big hospital — were required by law to head for the nearest facility to stabilize patients. That was Stanley.

With her boss's approval, she began writing letters to all the ambulance companies nearby. Very soon they were bringing their patients to Stanley.

"Over the next three years we picked up business and went from a hospital that looked like it was going to close to one that was opening a new facility in June of 2002, funded by a local community drive and a couple of local·wealthy people. It's state of the art: a clinical lab, a nursing home, a hospital, an ER. The community even rallied to try to pay for American physicians at competitive prices. The hospital had been hiring foreign interns at a cut rate to save expenses. The foreigners would do it for three years and move on. That was a problem. Patients weren't satisfied with the foreign interns. Not only was there a rapid turnover, but even while they stayed, there was very little communication between the patient and doctor. Because of the language barriers, patients couldn't understand them."

Worse, she would frequently be on call, up all night, while the non-English speaking doctors got to sleep through the night. That ended when the new building opened and Trinity hired two UND graduates from the Fargo family practice program to share the duties.

Dr. Mayer now spends most of her time trying to expand the clinic in New Town.

"I was well trained at UND and I'm a good diagnostician," she says. And with those tools and my work ethic, I can make good things happen in this community. I'm helping patients get what they need for a better life — not just putting Band-Aids on them and shooing them on their way. It's not hard for me to do, because these people I treat out here are my family and friends and relatives."

But early on, a lot of her colleagues told her that might not be such a good idea.

"Before I came out here, there were lots of discouraging words," she says. "It would be too hard to be objective to take care of your own, was their argument. But I made that commitment and a promise as a pre-med student. So I'm gonna make good on my word. I've got to try. I'm going to take the risk that, yes, I do realize this is going to be hard. People thought I might have done myself in. There're very few Indian women in family practice in this nation. I probably could have paved a wonderful path in Denver or Albuquerque. But I chose to come back out here. Why would someone like me spend all these years obtaining these skills and go to the big city and take care of people who I don't know — people I probably never will know and probably don't care that much about? It seems to make better sense to take those skills and come home and take care of people who really need it and you don't have to teach yourself to care. You just do naturally. I think that makes for better medicine. I had to try it."

Not that it's been easy. The first six months were really hard, she says, because her clinic competes with the Indian Health Service. Fort Berthold is the only open reservation in the state — meaning there are non-Indian businesses allowed to operate there, including Trinity. None of the four other North Dakota reservations allows such competition for health care.

"But many Indian people do not like to go to Health Service facilities," she says. "I think they're under-funded, their doctors are overworked, the providers rotate in and out, and there's no continuity. Patients don't like to see a different doctor every time they come. They get the feeling, 'Well they don't care about me. Why should I tell them anything anyway?' And they have to sit and wait for long periods of time because the place is understaffed. It's not uncommon for them to wait two to three hours."

Tribal leaders don't always agree with her, she says, and they often prefer that tribal members use the IHS facilities. Although the politics has been difficult at times, she has chosen to remain to prove a point.

"Not to myself," she says, "but to prove I can do what I said I'd do. I'm going to put my nose to the grindstone, run this clinic, and be the best quality provider I can be for all those who decide to come here. Anyone who wants to come here will be well cared for. In time, just by being better at what we do, we will win the patients."

So far, she has drawn a large clientele from Medicaid and Medicare subscribers.

"These people don't have to come here. They can go where they want. I told the tribal leaders to let the patients decide where they want to go. I told them they could not compete with me. I'm an old basketball player. And the way I look at it, I've got a team that can go to the state championship with first-class equipment, staff, uniforms, the works. And they've got a team that's not going to get out of districts. And they can't play ball against me."

She likes sports metaphors and told her nurses when she took over, "I'm the coach, this is the way we're gonna play ball. This is the game. If you don't like it, I want you to go and find another team where you'll be happy. You need to be happy here, to do what we are supposed to be doing. Let's have some fun and let's get to work."

She draws her patients not only from the tribe and reservation but from afar. "A lot of non-Indians around here — farmers and ranchers — knew my father. They come to see me. Surprisingly, I have a large, white-male patient population. Makes me feel I'm doing what I'm supposed to be doing."

In the meantime, she lives in town with her mother. She attends all community events, does her Lewis and Clark presentations, and sponsors local children who don't have the funds to attend basketball camp. And it isn't unusual for people to knock on her door and ask to borrow a few dollars for gas.

"I know these people. It might take them a year or two to pay it back, but they pay it back."

But not always in cash. Several patients pay Dr. Mayer in craft works. One patient's transmission went out on her car, her only means of transportation. She didn't have the $500 to fix it, so she brought in a handmade war bonnet and a hand-stitched star quilt and sold them to Mayer for $500.

"The lady goes and gets her car fixed so she can take care of her family and get to her job," she says. "She's happy. I'm happy. Everybody's happy. I do a lot of that."

As generous as she is, however, there's one plea for which she has no soft spot.

"I don't give to alcoholics asking for money." She says. "They know that. It's taken them awhile to learn that. But they don't bother to ask any more. In fact, when they see my little red Jeep driving around, they run. I'll call the BIA cops on them."

It's a topic that turns this young doctor from cheerfulness to flinty hardness.

"We don't own the book on the disease of alcoholism," she says, "but we do have a problem here. If they want help they know they can go down to the local café and charge a meal to me. If a kid in high school wants to go to basketball camp, I tell them I will sponsor you if you do the best you can. But if I ever find out you're drinking, I'll never support you again. That's the rule.

"I don't think there's anybody on this reservation who hasn't been touched by alcohol. My grandfather drank himself to death. He was forty-two. My grandmother and grandfather had six children. The youngest was a boy who died of alcoholism. When my grandmother remarried, she had six more kids. Two committed suicide under the influence of alcohol.

"Being the only doctor who provides after-hours care, I see

numerous drug and alcohol overdoses, and beatings and rapes. I see all the social ills of alcohol abuse between 2 A.M. and 5 A.M. on Friday and Saturday night. I've always had a zero tolerance toward alcohol. When I first came out here, I told alcoholics if they were rude or used vulgar language or were abusive or tried to injure the staff here, we would put them out. I just don't tolerate it. There are no better manipulators than alcoholics. They used to be able to come in here to the clinic and get a bath and get pampered. I don't go for that. Being drunk is not a medical emergency."

Very neatly, it all ties back to Lewis and Clark and, of course, Good Medicine.

"Two hundred years ago, when Lewis and Clark came here, they came with fifty gallons of whiskey that the federal government intended they use in negotiations with tribal people. It's documented. They did it with the Teton Sioux and the Omaha Indians. When they arrived at Canonball, North Dakota, they came to the Arikara nation. They offered whiskey — and it was not diluted. The Arikara response was that no friend would give us something that would make us act like fools. As Lewis and Clark moved further on, they met the Mandan and then the Hidatsa — and all three tribes said no to alcohol.

"I tell people here that their ancestors knew this was not a good thing. I tell the same story to my alcoholics after they've sobered up. Being an Indian person is not drinking liquor. For our ancestors never drank. They realized its devastation. Today all I have to say is that this is a terrible disease. It's worse than diabetes. At least for that you have medicines. Alcohol has no medicines. And I tell them: I will not tolerate you bringing in babies you can't take care of and not being able to hold a job. You are killing us economically on our reservation."

But even as she pounds home her points on alcoholism, she's able to catch herself and revert back to that family doc.

"'Hey!'" she hollers to a mother and two children just walking past her open office door. "We'll see you boys! See you, Virgil!'"

She pauses, smiling, "They're quite the crew, aren't they?"

But then, relentlessly, like her father, she is back.

"There's so much more than just getting through medical school to being a good doctor. It's not the hours, it's not the medical knowledge. It takes commitment and caring for a physician to come to a small town and help it thrive. I just want to be a part of that. We need to see the Indian people move forward. It's going to happen through people like me."

Doctors of the Windshield

24

In 1963, when Jerry Sailer was about to graduate from Baylor University's School of Medicine in Houston — where he'd gone after completing his first two years at the University of North Dakota — he signed up for a post-graduate internship in general practice.

Almost immediately he was summoned to the Baylor dean's office.

The dean was extremely disappointed in him. He told Sailer, "We can get you into Johns Hopkins or Massachusetts General. We'd like for you to consider going into academic medicine or a sub-specialty or research."

Sailer said no.

"I chose the internship because I want to do general practice in a small town," he explained to the dean. Specifically, he added, a small town in his home state of North Dakota.

The dean at Baylor couldn't believe his ears. "Well, I guess we've wasted some time with you here at Baylor," he said. "If you want to be a missionary, why not just go to Africa?'"

Such was — and perhaps still is — the attitude about rural medicine: nobody goes into rural medicine, or if they do, it's because they couldn't hack it in the big cities where the money and prestige are to be found.

But Sailer, along with his UND classmate Paul Retzer, founded a clinic in one of the most isolated parts of the state that stands today as the miracle model of how rural medicine can be as sophisticated as the urban variety.

Today, some forty years after Sailer set out to tilt at windmills, the West River Regional Medical Center in Hettinger, a town of only 1,300 souls down in the rolling, unadorned plains in the southwestern corner of the state, employs fourteen doctors with impeccable credentials. The technology in the clinic is as up to date as — and in many cases more modern — than in any large city hospital. The staff includes a full-time surgeon and radiologist and doctors specializing in pediatrics and family practice medicine. Attached to the clinic is a small hospital, owned and operated by its doctors and staffed by a thriving nursing service.

But how can a town of only 1,300 keep such a clinic going? The answer is, it can't. And that leads to the element that makes the Hettinger clinic unique and so successful. For instead of making patients come to them, these doctors go to the patients.

Each day the Hettinger doctors, after making hospital rounds, drive from forty to 100 miles to one of nine satellite clinics to treat patients. Their income is far below what they can make in a large city. Their hours are horrendous — twelve- and fourteen-hour days are common; Sailer put in 110-hour weeks when he started the clinic. Yet the doctors at this clinic show no signs of flagging morale or of giving up. Just the contrary: many of them have been there twenty-five and thirty years and all of them seem quite content with their lifestyle.

"We'd always tell the doctors we recruited that the economics would be way worse than if they went to a larger place," says Sailer.

"That they would work longer days and work a lot harder. But the return was that here you could really make a difference. I know that there are a lot of doctors in the cities who see it as a business, but medicine is a mission."

Sailer says he learned that at UND, where the attitude laid down by men like Dean Ted Harwood and John Vennes was completely different from that of Baylor and other large city medical schools.

"We developed a sense of mission in that many of us knew that if it weren't for that medical school we would not have had an opportunity to become doctors," he says. "Many of us felt that we should try to return to North Dakota and repay the people of the state who made that possible. And it was when I was at UND that I developed a philosophy that rural people should be able to have the same kind of medical care as anyone else."

Sailer was raised in rural North Dakota and he wanted to practice in an isolated place that was lacking in medical facilities. Hettinger certainly fit the bill. When he arrived, Hettinger was little more than a triage station for Rapid City, South Dakota, and Bismarck. His friend Paul Retzer was practicing alone at the time, and the two established a partnership.

Burning with idealism, the two thought they could probably build up enough of a patient base to support the practice of good medicine. But the first year or so was extremely frustrating. They were battling long-time prejudices against rural medicine that had even infected their patients.

"The habit was for people to go to Bismarck or the Mayo Clinic in Rochester, Minnesota. There was an old expression back then: 'You have to go through the clinic.' The general idea was that modern medicine couldn't be practiced in small towns. They'd never experienced it. There had never been a surgery done in Hettinger. It wasn't even common for people to have a physical exam in a small town."

The town's only clinic was at the local Lutheran Hospital, which offered minimal services. "It was a place to go to find out if you were sick," Sailer says. "And if you were, then you were sent on to someplace else."

Worse, the hospital wouldn't invest in any equipment. Sailer, who had done specialized training in general surgery, wanted to perform surgeries in the hospital. But he needed a portable X-ray machine. The hospital refused to buy one.

"I thought of pulling out," he says. "In fact, I remember a meeting Paul and I had. We decided we were going to make every effort to get the equipment and services we needed here. And if people didn't partake, then we would just not fight it."

He and Retzer took out a loan and bought their X-ray machine and installed it in the hospital. They ended up buying lots more equipment and supplies and finally approached local community leaders for help.

Hearing and feeling the zeal of the two doctors, the town established a fund and raised enough money to buy the hospital outright. With the transfer of ownership came a new community spirit toward the idea of having and using its own medical center.

To make it work, of course, the two doctors needed to draw in more patients. It was about that time that a delegation of citizens from the small town of New England, about forty-five miles north of Hettinger, approached Sailer and Retzer. For years, New England had benefited from a clinic sponsored by the Sears & Roebuck Foundation. But their Sears doctor had retired and they weren't able to attract another. They'd gone up to Dickinson, a moderate-sized city about twenty-five miles north, and asked doctors there if they could come down one or two days a week. They were told no, patients come to doctors, not the other way around.

But in Hettinger the two doctors said they'd do it and began spending a day each week in a small office they set up. This happened at a time in history when the Space Race between America and Soviet Union was in full swing and the term "satellite" was an everyday word.

Sailer and Retzer thought the term perfectly described their outlying office in New England. The weekly visits weren't easy, though. Sailer remembers one day treating ninety-six patients in the New England office.

Without realizing it, the two doctors were making history of their own with the first-of-its-kind medical satellite clinic.

"Jerry Sailer came out here in the early 1960s and he saw a tremendous health need," says Jim Long, CEO and administrator of the West River clinic. "He wasn't one of those people who thought if you build it they will come. The people were out in these small communities. They were suffering. They didn't drive into the big city to see a doctor. They didn't go anywhere. They couldn't take time away from their work. Jerry thought we needed to build a system that addressed that and to build a patient population base so we could have the technology and services people deserve. The idea was to provide urban-style medicine in a rural environment."

Not only was the concept effective, it also relieved some of the exhausting practices that had crept into the old way of doing things in rural medicine.

"The idea of a being in a little town with two docs who are overworked and on call all the time and crabby, we could see that wasn't where it's at," says Dr. Terry R. Mack. "If you're going to have multi-specialty group with a lot of skills, you just have to go out to the people. The only way to do it is by satellite."

It wasn't long before a second satellite was added, this one in Lemmon, South Dakota, about forty miles from Hettinger and just across the state line. It was the first assignment of Hettinger's newest recruit, Dr. Mack, and it got off to a fast start very literally overnight.

"When I came here," says Mack, who has been in Hettinger almost thirty years, "there were two docs in Lemmon and they got into a fight. I showed up there one day and the administrator of the local hospital said, 'Please come and make rounds.' He said the two doctors had sued each other and both of them had left town in the middle of the night. So I started coming there and tried to help them out. When one of those two doctors came back, the hospital asked me not to do rounds. I said, 'Hell no. Let the patients decide. I'm not going away.'"

Nor was Sailer, who kept recruiting new doctors for potential expansion to new satellite clinics. "He tried to instill into his recruits his enthusiasm for rural medicine," says Long. "Not the superficial stuff, but the part where you can really make a difference."

Yet, so enervating were Sailer's struggles, that in his middle fifties he finally burned out.

"I spent so many hours working in medicine that I wasn't home a whole lot," he recalls. "As my kids got older, I really began to wish I could have spent more time with them. My son got a degree in agriculture economics and he wanted to ranch. I thought what an opportunity to spend every day with him. I was fifty-five and I just made the decision to ranch with him. We had such an outstanding group of doctors here, I felt if I left it wouldn't hurt the delivery of medical care."

Without realizing it, Sailer had been bitten by the ranching bug that he had often observed in his patients. "From the time I got here," he says, "the kind of patients I saw were different. These ranchers never wanted to take a vacation. It never seemed important to have a nest egg so they could retire. They were just happy doing what they were doing. I slowly got absorbed into that culture."

He admits he was also bothered more and more by government regulations and medical legal considerations. "We were doing more and more just to protect ourselves. I had started in an era where you never even thought of that. You just did what was best for patients."

While his retirement from medicine made sense to his colleagues, his absence had a considerable impact.

"His retirement was the biggest loss to medicine in the country," says Dr. Robert E. Grossman, another three-decade veteran at Hettinger. "Jerry had such vision."

Still, the West River Regional Medical Center went on and continues today with clinics in Mott, Bowman, Bison, Scranton, McIntosh, New England, Lemmon and Buffalo. It also has a podiatry clinic in Dickinson. It also continues to mystify big city doctors.

"People in the big cities don't understand how a town of 1,300 people could have this size operation," says Long. "They say, 'What do those doctors do all day? Play a lot of golf?' They have no idea about satellites and what we really do."

Today, he says, the general perception of rural medicine is still "a small, fifty-bed hospital with no technology, no support and usually a doctor who doesn't have his ducks in row. Someone who can't get a job somewhere else. That certainly isn't the situation here. Our physicians could go anywhere and be successful."

But recruiting them has always been the key to success and, at the same time, the trickiest part of the whole operation. Getting young doctors to come all the way out to the middle of nowhere requires magic. But, as luck would have it, there's lots of magic to go around here. Take the case of Dr. Mark S. Kristy, the clinic's radiologist, a newcomer of only seven years.

"I talked to Jim Long on the phone one day when I was looking for a job," says Kristy, "but I didn't seriously consider it. One fella in my training group had been in the Air Force and was stationed at Minot. He said, 'You know, Kristy, I don't give you much advice, but there's one place I'll tell you not to go and that's North Dakota.' Everything else he told me was right."

After some persuasion by Long, and Kristy's perception that radiology jobs suddenly were drying up, Kristy reluctantly flew into Dickinson and came down to Hettinger to look around. He had a terrible cold when he arrived, but one of the clinic's physicians, Dr. Robert W. Beattie, gave him some cough syrup. Then he was invited to dinner at the local country club. It happened to be the night of the annual roast banquet where practical jokes and laughs were the main item on the menu.

"I ended up with a really good impression of the place," says Kristy. "I called my wife and said, 'You're not going to believe this, but I think I want us to move to North Dakota.' Really, there was no comparison with any other place. The obvious difference was the people. You just could tell. This place was head and shoulders above the rest."

As for Long, he was convinced Kristy was the right man even before he arrived. "I got him on the phone, this young resident really anxious for a job, and he says to me, 'I'm sorry, can I call you back? I have a patient on the table and ready to go. I really need to take care of the patient first.' 'Sure,' I said. I hung up and told everyone, 'I think I found the right guy. He said the patient comes first.'"

Almost every doctor in the clinic has a similar shaggy dog story about how they ended up where they never expected to be.

Beattie remembers reluctantly coming to Hettinger for a job interview only because his preceptor in medical school, Dr. John P. Joyce, had worked at the clinic and browbeat him to coming down at least for a look-see.

"It was a long way from anywhere," recalls Beattie. "I said, 'Thanks, John, but I don't know.' But I did fly down there for the day. I got out of the airplane and they'd just had eight years of drought. It had to be ninety-five, the dust was blowing, it was dry. But I got here and started walking through the building and I said, 'Wow, this is really a neat place; they do a lot of neat things here.' You know, when doctors think about going to a rural setting, it means they have to think about changing their practice. The idea of putting up with less. Less technology, less everything. Here, though, in a real small town, I could practice medicine the way I was taught. And then some."

The "then some" factor that has wowed so many doctors is the idea that in a town of 1,300 a clinic could be so technically up to date on almost any gizmo modern medicine has devised. For example, West River was the second site in the entire state of North

Dakota to purchase a spiral CT scanner. It was the first to embrace the concept of labor-delivery-recovery-post and has built its own LDRP room in the clinic. Almost anything that can be done in a large city hospital can be done in Hettinger.

"We have internists and a surgeon and pediatricians and a good radiologist," says Mack. "It's quite amazing we are able to do what we do. If you came in here very sick, I'll bet you my last dollar we'd make a diagnosis quicker than they would in a big city. I've had it happen. Someone comes in with a horrible problem. In twenty-four hours we have the diagnosis made and the guy is on the road to recovery. In the big city, you'd order an X-ray or CAT scan. Someone will say we can't do it today. You have twelve people ahead of you. Then you have to wait to see this or do that. We can cut through the crap."

Even so, many big city doctors develop a condescending view of rural doctors — whom they dismissively refer to as LMDs, for local medical doctor. Often, small town doctors, limited in equipment and resources, act mostly as a triage for big city emergency rooms — the way Hettinger operated when Sailer and Retzer first came to town. City doctors felt that rural doctors simply dumped their complicated patients on their doorstep.

"But we don't dump our patients on the ER's of the bigger city hospitals," says Grossman. "We keep an interest in all our patients."

In fact, there's often a reluctance to refer a patient for specialized care in a larger hospital.

"When I was a third-year medical student who had transferred from UND to the University of Minnesota," says Dr. Kent Hoerauf, "one thing that impressed me was how a patient could come in with a seemingly simple procedure and get caught in a quagmire of complications and end up dying. I saw that more than once. They'd come in, develop an infection, which would lead to an abscess and another procedure and then another complication. And then pretty soon there's more. And then the patient didn't make it. I was really astounded. How could that happen?

"One thing I learned: there are some patients who are very fragile and who tend to be more prone to complications. The big tertiary hospital centers have a certain pattern of referrals. They're going to get the hard cases that the general internist or GP feels are more complicated. We termed it the ivory tower — the epitome of learning and research. If you can't figure it out, you send your patient to the ivory tower. And so, being one of the little soldiers in the ivory tower, you kind of sit alongside. And there are certainly successes, there's no doubt about it. Yet being exposed to some of the complications that can occur, you really wonder how often that can happen. When I'm looking at things in my daily experiences now, I know that the ivory tower may not always be the answer. I kind of see some safety issues in how I approach my patients. You have to be careful what you do and how you refer. Because they might not come back."

That fierce connection to a patient is hard for some doctors to feel, says Grossman.

"Overall, there's a reason why lots of doctors don't come to Hettinger. You have to do all of these things. It's hard to train someone to accept that kind of responsibility."

And it's also hard to fight that negative image rural medicine has with its big city colleagues.

"There's almost an expectation that the quality in rural medicine will be less," says Joyce. "But a C-section should be done as well in rural areas as they are in big cities. My patients should have the same expectations of quality here as in a big city."

The patients themselves are another part of the rural challenge.

"We have an older population," says Joyce, "because younger people are leaving the area. Because of the economic downturn and the repeated droughts, there's been an increase in grief and loss and pain in this area. With that comes more anger and bitterness. I'd say that's probably different than in Bismarck, where you'd have a much younger practice. I don't think doctors there are aware of the rural grief that's out there."

Because the town of Lemmon can't get a psychiatrist to locate there, Joyce, who serves as medical director for the regional mental health center, sees troubled adults and kids. He's following in the footsteps of Dr. Roger Schauer, a former Hettinger doctor who now works in Grand Forks with the medical school. Schauer did a fellowship in psychiatry and adolescent and child psychiatry, and when he left, asked Joyce to continue his work.

"I had to become adept at psychiatric illnesses," says Joyce, whose work is monitored by a psychiatrist in Bismarck.

"People out here are physically tough and stoic," says Kristy. "They have work to do and they don't have time to mess around with a pain, even though it's been aching for three months. Occasionally I see things most doctors only see in textbooks because people put off coming to a doctor for so long and their problem gets quite advanced."

Kristy, the radiologist, and Dr. Bill Elder, the surgeon, are the only two Hettinger doctors who spend all their time at the clinic itself. Every one of the other doctors puts in what is called "windshield time," driving from the clinic to any of the nine satellite offices. Many of those offices are staffed also by live-in physician assistants — trained in the UND MEDEX program begun by Bob Eelkema. Jim Long works the schedule so that each satellite office gets a variety of medical specialties each week, and can rely on a certain doctor who specializes in pediatrics or family medicine being at a certain clinic on a certain day.

"Most of our satellite clinics are about forty miles away," says Beattie. "If you can keep that windshield time to less than forty-five minutes, most people don't see it as a burden."

Mondays Beattie goes to Lemmon. Tuesdays he's either in Faith or Buffalo or precepting with students in Bismarck. Wednesdays he's in Bowman. He spends Thursdays in Hettinger and Fridays in Mott.

"It's stability for the patients," he says. "They can count on a certain doctor being there on a regular basis. And to me, being on the road is a time for quiet reflection. You can process what you did in the morning. You can get things organized in your head as you move toward the clinic. Lots of times, coming back from Bowman, I get to Bucyrus and I don't even remember going by Reeder. You can kind of shut things off."

But as the population decreases in the area, Long says he has had to reach further and further into the hinterland to find enough of a patient base to keep the clinic viable.

"We keep pushing the envelope and edges as far as we can," says Long. "But there is a limit to windshield time. You figure, if you go to Buffalo, which is ninety miles away, and you spend an eight-hour day there, then you've got three hours of travel. Plus, you have your rounds. We do them in the morning and evening. So Dr. Hoerauf, for example, will end up starting his day at 6:30 A.M., and still be here at 8 or 9 P.M."

"It's not always an easy thing to do," says Grossman. "But it's better to have a doctor travel those miles to see elderly patients than to make them come in to see us. We see it as what we should be doing. It's a philosophy."

And without question, that philosophy is doled out along with medical wisdom to students from the University of North Dakota's School of Medicine, who are trained here as part of its unique community medicine approach. Unlike states with larger populations, UND cannot rely on a large university hospital to train its students. Rather than surrender to this perceived weakness and close its two-year school back in 1973, the university turned it into a strength. It expanded to a four-year, degree-granting school, and now trains its students and residents by placing them in university clinics and in supporting medical facilities around the state.

"From the very beginning," says Sailer, "we were into having students come here. We felt we could provide a rural experience for students and, hopefully, they would be interested in going to small communities. We also saw it as a way for us to get to know the best ones who came through and continue the recruiting process."

The West River clinic usually has several students going through a specific rotation. In fact, student training there is the way almost all of the current Hettinger doctors first learned of the place.

"It's quite remarkable what the physicians at Hettinger have done for the medical school," says Dr. George Magnus Johnson, the former pediatrics chair at UND and now a roving instructor for the school. "It's amazing how those students are thriving. They're getting a superb education down there."

"We get some of the most stellar students from UND down here," says Dr. Kristy, one of the few Hettinger doctors who is not a UND grad. "They are just wonderful people. They're all extremely bright, much smarter than I am."

One of the things that has impressed Johnson is the attendance by clinic doctors at the weekly staff meetings. "At 7 A.M. in Hettinger, every single physician is there and also every nurse practitioner. And that's unusual. At that kind of meeting in Fargo you'd never ever get all the physicians there. But they were all there. And that's sort of a paradigm of what the rural areas of the state thought they could do with the medical school as opposed to the thinking of doctors in Fargo."

In stating its case for a four-year medical school to the state's doctors thirty years ago, the university argued that a community-based school would actually give students a better education than if they went to a big city university hospital. They'd be able to work one-on-one with doctors, rather than being part of a large group of students trained not by doctors but by residents — essentially graduate students. Many doctors scoffed at the notion. They had been trained very well at large hospitals, they said, and couldn't see how any other method would work.

But Dr. Mack, who graduated from the old two-year medical

school in Grand Forks and transferred to the University of Colorado, smiles ruefully at the big city theory.

When he got to Colorado, he says, the CU students had already been given the choice rotation assignments. The transfers were left with the ones nobody wanted. His first rotation was in the sub-specialty neurosurgery.

"I never saw such a bunch of jerks in all my life," he says. "They really didn't care about the student. The student was a little better than dirt under their fingernails, basically.

"The first day I was there, the big case was a pituitary tumor that this hotshot neurosurgeon was going to take out. It was done with an operating microscope. So I scrub into surgery. This guy is a real prima donna. He had me stand next to him and hold this retractor and all he would say was 'too hard' or 'too soft.' It was that way the whole time. Eight hours later I hadn't drunk anything, eaten anything, gone to the bathroom. I still had the retractor. And he's still yelling at the nurses and yelling at everybody. And he finally gets done. I'm tired. And I haven't learned a thing except this guy wants to yell at me. I'm trying to please him but it's not possible. This guy is impossible to please.

"The surgical scrub nurse says, 'Doctor, the sponge count is not correct. We are one sponge short. Is it okay with you if I X-ray the patient's head after you're done closing? Or do you want to look for the sponge?' And he says, 'With all of the people in and out of here today, I'm sure one of those damn pathologists has it stuck onto his vest. I know I didn't leave one.' And so he closes the incision. So, as soon as I get rid of the retractor, I run into the bathroom and I drink a bunch of water. I get my clothes on and I'm thinking this is the worst day of my life. I've never spent such a wasted day in all my life. And as I'm walking out of the place, the second-year resident yells out the window. He says, 'Terry, you've got to come back. We've got to go back in and get the sponge out. The sponge is in the guy's head.' And I'm thinking, what a jerk. I am never going to be a doctor like that guy. He never even looked for it. That influenced me plenty. I thought how in the hell can somebody be like this?"

But it wasn't only the jerk factor that turned him off. In that large Denver hospital, he says, "I never saw an appendectomy, a hernia repair, a colocystecomy, a D&C, any of the common surgical things. All I ever saw was stuff that you'd never see anywhere except at a university referral center. Pituitary tumors, bypass surgeries, valve replacements, all this high powered stuff. Never once did I see any bread and butter surgical stuff. And it just turned me off, all these prima donna people running around doing this high powered stuff.

"Then I came back to Hettinger and here's Jerry Sailer fixing three hernias and doing a gall bladder and an appendix before noon. And doing a good job and people were happy and people lived and everybody was doing good."

Kent Hoerauf has similar memories from his transfer year at Minnesota.

"At the University of Minnesota, there was no direction. You had no objectives. You were just kind of out there to get a feel for what you were supposed to do. You were grilled by attending physicians when you made formal rounds each week. They'd ask questions which often weren't clear. You'd stumble and be embarrassed. It was just a painful experience."

In medical parlance, that practice is known as "pimping."

"In a lot of places," says Mack, "the students are purposely asked questions that are kind of impossible. They just let 'em squirm. Nobody here would do that. We treat them like we would want to be treated."

"My son is a senior med student in this program," adds Joyce. "He graduated from Notre Dame. Basically, I told him when he applied that the only school you should consider is North Dakota. You'll get a better education. I thought of myself floating along in that third year. Here you can get that great one-on-one teaching and develop a mentorship in the third and fourth year with an attending doctor that you cannot get in the big time traditional setting. I had wonderful mentors at UND. I saw a lot of happy, contented people practicing medicine and being generous."

Hoerauf was a medical student during the debate those many years ago about whether to fund a four-year medical school. He wrote letters of support to the State Legislature and thinks North Dakotans got a bargain

"There's nowhere you can get more education for your dollar than at North Dakota," says Hoerauf. "I would challenge any med school to match UND's numbers as far as returning our grads to North Dakota. At the same time, it's a sparsely populated state and paying for education is a tremendous burden on John Q. Public. So I felt I really needed to come back to North Dakota and invest back into the state what I received in education."

Not that teaching students is the easiest thing in the world.

"Absolutely, it's a burden," says Grossman. "Sugarcoat it all you want. But to be a good teacher is an incredible responsibility. You just don't have 'em walk along behind you. You have to teach them constantly and expose them to different things, make them realize what's important and what's not. It's an enormous physical and emotional burden to do it right."

"If I have a student," says Mack, "I'm always worried that for them it will be a meaningful experience. To just have them around as deadwood doesn't work. You've got to make them think and make them work. I make them see the patient before me and try to diagnose what's wrong and formulate a treatment plan. Then I let them order the tests and make them get involved in the patient's care. Then I've got to smooth it over and get the rough edges off. Of course, I've got to check it out with the patient ahead of time that it's okay. It's a lot more work. The amount of calories expended by the end of the day is going to be greater. But I'm glad they're here. What the hell — how did I learn?"

If the quality of medicine and teaching in Hettinger is on

everyone's mind, so too is the quality of life. The population of this rural prairie town is declining rapidly, but it hasn't yet had an impact on its sense of humor. The town boasts it is the home of the world's shortest St. Patrick's Day parade.

"We always have had trouble recruiting spouses," says Grossman. "There isn't a Marshal Fields or a fabulous theater here. You have to want to live out here to be here. It's a spiritual place, though. I had a brain tumor scare last year. Turned out to be nothing dangerous. But I spent a lot of time walking at night, smelling the air and looking at those buttes. I need space. I need to see long distances, and sunrises. Part of life is to accept who you are and what you are. I realize this place is the best-kept secret in the world. It's an incredible place to live and to grow."

In fact, says Joyce, growth is the hidden treasure here.

"You live in a fishbowl," he says. "I know the skeletons in a lot of family closets. I know a lot of family secrets. And they know my family secrets — that's the problem. People can see your weaknesses and screwups. You have to have a lot of personal growth over the years. If you do, you can achieve a sense of community. But you have to be non-judgmental. You have to be forgiving. You have to be a lot of things it's easy to forget about when you live in anonymity in a larger city."

One benefit of the lack of anonymity, says Hoerauf, is a unique ability to measure your success.

"As time goes on, you can see where you make a difference. This guy walking down the street. You treated him for heart disease. His heart is up and running. He's functional. He's continuing to work. And he contributes to his family and his town. It's something that med students don't realize when they're in Fargo. They just drive down the street and everything is anonymous. You get a different relationship in a small community."

You also get different hobbies.

"When I moved up here I didn't hunt," says Kristy. "I do now.

It's a big part of life up here. Up here, people take their kids rattlesnake hunting. Sure, there are things I'd like to do more regularly — go to fancy restaurants or a show or an opera or a symphony. Everybody needs to take time off and get out of Dodge. But those are diversions. It's not like I sit at home pining away for that sort of thing. The positives outweigh the negatives. I've got my garden and my dog. And I've got a big metal out-building. Everybody kids me that it's the biggest in town. And I will get it filled up with crap, I promise you."

Already it contains a vintage pink Nash Rambler, circa 1960, that Kristy bought at an auction and swears he is going to restore someday.

But even with personal growth and Nash Ramblers and a snakeskin on the wall, there would still be something lacking in Hettinger, say these doctors, if it weren't for the most mysterious element of all.

Everybody in this clinic gets along.

Understand, they are quick to point out, that doesn't mean they always agree with each other. But to have so many doctors in one group practice staying for ten, twenty and thirty years without killing each other is the intangible that has made this place most unusual.

"We acknowledge there's more than one way of doing things," says Beattie. "And my way may be just a little bit different than your way, but we respect that in each other. We have a monthly business meeting. Sometimes they get down and dirty and we call each other names. But you walk out as friends. You don't try to talk about each other behind their back. I know it's different than other places. You won't find very many groups of docs that have been together for any great length of time."

"We basically pull the rope together," adds Mack. "It's been a struggle. This isn't fertile ground for a medical group. It's hard to make things work but we've made it work."

Joyce thinks the clinic's harmony exists because the doctors in the group are more outward focused than inward. He is not the only one who describes his work as a mission and not just a job.

"I don't think there's a group in North Dakota that has the chemistry we have down here," says Joyce. "There is an attitude of mutual respect, of mutual empowerment to be the best. We have a high standard here. There's a lot of idealism. When you work in a negative setting, it takes away a lot of energy. And it takes energy to get up in the middle of the night to take care of sick people. Of course, none of us really prefers to take care of sick people in the middle of the night, but down here we're blessed. It's only one in seven nights. I have a healthy group, and so I have energy to do more."

As idealistic as it all sounds, one huge negative looms over Hettinger. The sociological term for it is depopulation. The great Northern Plains have seen many a plague over the years, but this one is taking people and not just crops.

"Depopulation is the one thing that scares us," says Grossman. "We always used to say if things are tough, then if you just work harder, spend longer hours, we'll get better and be able to sustain. But the depopulation thing I have no answer for. I always said we couldn't go more than forty-five miles for a satellite clinic because of the stress on the doctor. Well, we're approaching 100 plus miles now.

"And you have to have a certain level of technology to have good young doctors come here and stay. We're at a point with depopulation where we might not be able to afford all of that technology. If so, we'll blow away in the wind. You can't expect a good hot internist to come out here and do nothing but triage. You've got to be able to do CAT scans and nuclear medicine and blood gases and drug levels. You have to be able to provide that."

Currently the clinic serves a potato-shaped service area that covers roughly 25,000 square miles of southwestern North Dakota and northwestern South Dakota. In that area live less than 20,000 people. In last fifteen years, the area has lost a fifth of its population. Twenty years ago, 299 babies were delivered at the clinic in a single year; last year, only seventy-five.

"Young people aren't here having babies," says Mack. "It's happening with my own children. I don't think they're coming back. Oh, we're still busy. We have a lot of older people. But that comes to an end. In the past, what we've done is put our tentacles out a little further. But now we are bumping up against Bismarck, Dickinson, Rapid City. We have already filled the void. It's unrealistic to think we would take patients away from Rapid City or Bismarck. The question is, can we renew ourselves? I don't know. Service is the primary mission of this place, not profit. Can we continue to be fourteen docs or are we ten? If we're ten, can we continue to do everything we're doing now?"

It's the same question Jim Long asks himself each day.

"It's a concern," he says. "With our change in demographics, we keep expanding. The facility and services will survive. But something is going to change."

Whatever changes, the fixed star of this little town will remain shining on Sailer's clinic. "It was founded on a sense of mission," he says. "All physicians are going to be helpful to their patients most of the time, sometimes supremely helpful. But even beyond that, if you can raise the level of health care in an entire community, then you will have done something worthwhile, you won't have been just one of a large number of people who can easily be replaced — well, that's the message, the challenge."

APPENDIX 1

The Places and Faces

A classroom in the old Science building that housed the two-year School of Medicine.

Before it was demolished the old science building underwent many renovations, but it was never adequate.

The old science building, built in 1913, crowded the two-year medical school into its top floor.

Ted Harwood, M.D., dean of the two-year School of Medicine, didn't like the idea of expansion.

John Vennes, Ph.D., in early 70s. A key ally of expansion, he became acting dean of the medical school.

Wally Nelson, M.D., was a shrewd medical school administrator known for candor and cowboy boots.

Tom Clifford, a tough farm boy out of Langdon, was a war hero and beloved president of his alma mater.

Gary Dunn's charisma and suspect credentials had Clifford calling him a lovable fraud.

Young Bob Eelkema, M.D., became Dunn's best friend. The two broke lots of rules but won the day.

The infamous trip to East Lansing aboard this DC-3 fueled support for expansion and lots of hangovers.

Back in the day with Bud Shutt, M.D., Dick Smith, "Father of MEDEX" and Bob Eelkema.

Eelkema was known for his easy going style, his knack for winning grants and his organizational skill.

Tom Clifford (left) and Bob Eelkema first met on UND's handball courts. They've been pals ever since.

In 1947 the two-year medical school moved into its new building on campus.

An aerial view of the current site of the School of Medicine and Health Sciences in Grand Forks.

The main offices of the School of Medicine are in the old St. Michael's Hospital in Grand Forks.

This family practice clinic in Grand Forks was dedicated in 2001. It's used to train medical students.

APPENDIX 2

Notes and Index

Acknowledgments and Sources

The writing of *Good Medicine* required not only plenty of legwork, but the cooperation of scores of good people across multiple professions. I was overwhelmed by the cheerful willingness of people across North Dakota to help out, either by generously listening to the labored questions only an Easterner could think up, or by showing me the shortcuts across a state whose major roads go mostly on the compass, north, south, east, and west.

Special thanks, then, to Earl Strinden for the shortcut to Bismarck that took me through Buffalo and a fine lunch stop. Thanks to Jim Long for making sure I found the Enchanted Highway and all of those unbelievable steel structures. And thanks to Art Link for insisting I check out the Badlands. They've given me a year's worth of you-won't-believe-what-I-saw-out-there stories, and a yearning to keep coming back. In the meantime, Rykken Johnson and Dean Strinden and Bryce Streibel pointed me toward excellent books that brought me to a new appreciation for The Flickertail State.

Of course, I owe a great deal to Tom Clifford and Bob Eelkema for their trust, candor, patience and mostly their sense of humor. Thanks also to their wives, Gayle Clifford and Ginny Eelkema for opening their homes to me and treating me like family. I should state for the record that Tom and Bob kept to their word about their intentions. They chose to change nothing from the manuscript I turned in. They truly wanted the real story told, and had no interest in changing my characterization of events or people or to alter quotes to suit their own agenda. Therefore any errors in this volume are 100 percent my own.

My approach to this story was to interview as many people as I could who had a role to play back in 1971 through 1973. I also wanted to check out any public documentation of the events leading up to the passage of the bill in the Legislative Assembly that authorized the expansion of the School of Medicine.

Getting to those people and documents required a lot of logistical support. Much of it came from Sue Huus, one of the truly unsung heroes of the medical school. She is the kind of dedicated worker who gets done in a standard eight-hour day more than any four people could accomplish. Why do people like Sue never get paid the money of those four people? A longtime assistant to Dr. Eelkema, Sue did a good bit of the non-glamorous paperwork and research that helped Bob land all of those grants. Today Sue is still an invaluable resource, for she is foremost among those people who know where all the bodies are buried. During my trips to North Dakota, Sue helped me time and again with phone numbers, addresses, and logistical necessities, always with a brisk optimism that was contagious.

More help came from Dr. John Vennes. He was an eloquent spokesman at meeting after meeting in 1972–73, quietly convincing legislators and doctors and the general public of the critical need for a four-year medical school. More than one of the many persons I spoke to during my research said that without his unassuming, dignified and energetic help, the four-year school couldn't have happened. Dr. Vennes assisted me generously with invaluable background information about many of the key personalities involved.

Dr. George Magnus Johnson not only answered all of my questions and gave me a concise view of the medical school, he allowed me to tag along as he conducted rounds and spoke with students. If you look up "bedside manner" in a dictionary, you'll find a picture of the extraordinarily kind Dr. Johnson. Thanks also to his cousin, the radiologist Dr. Richard Johnson.

Dr. Monica Mayer was good enough to let me sit in her office in New Town and throw questions at her as she moved from one examination room after another. Her inspiring story of making it out of the reservation and then going back to help her people is a wonderful untold story — here, only hinted at — that does the medical school proud.

Dr. Mark Olson is the kind of doctor you wish you had. He has a sense of humor and a serious side that blend easily. Trusting and likable, he's what some people say you'd never find in a small town: a super doctor.

Jim Long in Hettinger, is a South Dakota boy, but no one holds it against him. Everybody has to be born somewhere. Jim is the kind of able administrator you'd expect to find working in one of those big city hospitals. Fortunately for the doctors and people of Hettinger, Jim likes it just where he is.

Bryce Streibel is the classic, dignified North Dakota politician. We sat in his tiny office in his home in Fessenden and talked for a couple of hours about life and how to deal with it. I learned more in that room than anyplace else about the goodness of the people of North Dakota — all from a strong man who fought the political wars for long decades and emerged clean and honorable.

Dean Strinden graciously took most of a Saturday to show me around the fascinating historic grounds near Williston, including old Fort Union. As we stood at the breathtaking juncture of the Yellowstone and Missouri Rivers, Dr. Strinden wondered aloud what magnificent city might have sprung up there had the government not held onto the land for so long and kept out development. Everywhere we went people recognized him with a friendly "Hi Doc."

Early on in my research, it was Dean's brother, Earl Strinden, one of several former Marines in this story, who helped me grasp the significance of the legislative committee created to study the four-year medical school issue. Earl, who was the Republican majority whip at the time, played a key role in making sure each member selected for that committee came in with a proclivity to favor expansion. Of course, when it came time to vote, Earl was there to whip things into shape.

Dr. Bill Harlan's insight into the mind and soul of Gary Dunn helped crystallize for me the essence of this story. Bill is one of those rare doctors who can speak a language that non-medical people can understand. He is able to measure a man without judging him, and to convey profound thoughts that resonate at the gut level.

Through my friend Rykken Johnson, I had heard much about Dr. Jim Brosseau before I met him. Like Johnson, Jim played some solid baseball in Drayton, leading to eight state titles and one national trophy between them and their teammates back in the day. Jim is the type of man who brims with knowledge and insight, while displaying none of the pretensions of one who does. He helped me determine where to go across North Dakota to find UND docs and filled in a lot of gaps in my feel for the story. A solid internist and Chair of the Department of Community Medicine at the School of Medicine from which he graduated, Jim is a North Dakota treasure.

Whenever the name of Art Link, the former governor is mentioned, people say without fail, "What a nice man." Over coffee served by his wife, Grace, Art laid out a vivid picture of an immigrant's life on the plains, recounting the arrival of his mother and father at Bismarck on a train in the early years of the twentieth century. The hard-work ethic he learned from his parents, who homesteaded near Bismarck, has been touched also by a gentleness and sensitivity you don't expect from a politician, let alone a governor. What a nice man.

Bob Eelekma's sister Ruth Morgan played another of those critical behind-the-scenes roles in this tale. As director of UND's Grants and Contracts, her number crunching helped brother Bob obtain and manage the key grants that funded this and other programs. She took the time to go over in some humorous detail the colorful events of that site visit to Grand Forks by NIH investigators in the summer of 1972.

Nancy Dunn was reluctant, at first, to talk about her late husband Gary. It was clear as we spoke near her new home in Seattle, that she had loved him. It was also evident that the frenetic style of life Gary led — and the unseen debts that mounted after his death — have affected her over the years. Still a vibrant, adventurous soul, Nancy was soon as open and candid as could be. She helped me understand Gary, without whom, many believe, the School of Medicine would have faded away.

Thanks to: Dr. Phil Dahl of Bismarck for his clear memory and his eagerness to help; Em Murray, another man of wisdom with a solid recall for details; Evan Lips, the former state senator and Bismarck mayor, who told about recruiting Tom Clifford into the Marines; Doug Fenderson, the honorable federal employee who knew where the money was buried and never forgot his roots in North Dakota.

A special thanks to the unbelievably dedicated doctors at Hettinger: Kent Hoerauf, Bill Elder, Terry Mack, Mark Kristy, Bob Grossman, Joseph Mattson, John Joyce and all the others, including and especially Dr. Jerry Sailer, the man who had the remarkable vision, and the guts to make it work.

C. Warner Litten is still active in politics, even in retirement.

When we met, he was head of the board that governed the retirement community where he now lives in Fargo. To many supporters of the medical school, Mr. Litten was the chief antagonist, but it's hard to see how this pleasant, engaging man could antagonize anyone. His personality proved to me the truth about what so many had said of North Dakota politics back then. You could think your political opponent was an absolute bonehead, but when the smoke had cleared you remained close colleagues and friends.

Though illness has made things difficult for Dr. Wally Nelson, now retired in Virginia, he still had his wry sense of humor when we visited, and a recollection of who did what when. He'll never stop smiling about the day his students at the medical school placed a large cowboy hat and a pair of boots on his desk — the lifelong symbols of this well respected man, saluted that day by those who knew a real one when they saw him.

Dick Davison was the coach of the Drayton baseball team that Jim Brosseau and Rykken Johnson starred on back when. Now living in Bismarck, Dick once worked for the state Board of Higher Education, and he helped me understand the politics of that body in 1972–73 and the nature of their power over the future of the medical school. Dick also helped identify some other key players in the Bismarck area, including John Olesrud, head of the Legislative Council, former senator and mayor Evan Lips, Emerson Murray, Dr. Keith Foster, Dr. Grandon Tolstedt and Vern Wagner. Each of them graciously gave of his time and helped me to move the story along.

Audrey D. Sumner, the untiring librarian in the archives of the Legislative Council in the Bismarck State Capitol, directed me to many important files I never would have known existed. She also directed a hungry stranger to several very decent restaurants in Bismarck. Many thanks.

Dr. Richard Conway, a former English professor at UND, and a long-time friend from my Colorado days, rescued this manuscript from its many deviations from common grammar, syntax and usage.

I'm told by Rykken Johnson — once a student of Dr. Conway at UND — that he was known as Captain Comma. Note to Johnson: Thanks for giving the manuscript your editor's eye as well. You're hereby advanced to Sergeant Semicolon.

And a special thanks to Robert Fischer, Ph.D., for shooting and providing most of the UND pictures found in Appendix 1

The following is a roundup of the books, reports and documents I relied on in putting this story together.

Books

A Brief History of North Dakota, by Herbert Clay Fish.
History of North Dakota, by Elwyn B. Robinson, 1966 University of Nebraska Press.
Pathways Through Life, 1983 by Bruce Streibel.

Reports

October 14, 1969: "Minutes Interstate Conference for Medical Education (Iowa, North Dakota, South Dakota, and Minnesota)." State Capitol, St. Paul, Minnesota.
"North Dakota Health Manpower," 1972, by Gary F. Dunn, North Dakota Medical Research Foundation.
Untitled "Informal history … of the Medical School in commemoration of its 75th Anniversary," by Vonda K. Redman, 1980. (Redman served as assistant to Dr. Tom Johnson, Dean of the Medical School.)
"The School of Medicine of the University of North Dakota: A Medical School in Transition," 1980, by Stanley W. Olson, M.D., University of North Dakota School of Medicine.
"Report to Legislative Council Medical Education Committee," October 24, 1980, University of North Dakota School of Medicine.

Articles

"The School of Medicine of the University of North Dakota," by H.E. French, MD, *Lancet*, February 1, 1932.

"Medical Education in North Dakota," by H.E. French, M.D., *Lancet*, 1936.

"North Dakota Medicine — A 70-year-span," by H.E. French, M.D., *Lancet*, January 1951.

"History of the University of North Dakota School of Medicine," by T.H. Harwood, M.D., *Lancet*, May 1960.

Public Records from the Archives of the Legislative Council

January 28, 1972: Memorandum, North Dakota Legislative Council, Committee on Medical Education and Services.

September 7, 1972: Memorandum, North Dakota Legislative Council, Committee on Medical Education and Services.

October 13, 1972: Memorandum, North Dakota Legislative Council, Committee on Medical Education and Services.

December 15, 1972: Memorandum, North Dakota Legislative Council, Committee on Medical Education and Services.

December. 22, 1972: Memorandum, North Dakota Legislative Council, Committee on Medical Education and Services.

January 5, 1973: Memorandum, North Dakota Legislative Council, Committee on Medical Education and Services.

January 9, 1973: Memorandum, North Dakota Legislative Council, Committee on Medical Education and Services.

January 19, 1973: Memorandum, North Dakota Legislative Council, Committee on Medical Education and Services.

January 22, 1973: Memorandum, North Dakota Legislative Council, Committee on Medical Education and Services.

1973 Legislative Council Report, "Medical Education and Services."

January 13, 1979: Memorandum, North Dakota Legislative Council, Committee on Medical Education and Services.

June 1979: "Background Memorandum on Study of Four Year

Medical Program of the University of North Dakota Medical School," North Dakota Legislative Council, Medical Education Committee.

October 16–17, 1979: Memorandum, North Dakota Legislative Council, Committee on Medical Education and Services.

February 28, 1980: "Memorandum to Medical School Task Force of the Legislative Council," from Stanley W. Olson, M.D., Consultant in Medical Education, University of North Dakota School of Medicine.

February 29, 1980: Memorandum, North Dakota Legislative Council, Committee on Medical Education and Services.

June 16, 1980: Memorandum, North Dakota Legislative Council, Committee on Medical Education and Services..

October 24, 1980: Memorandum, North Dakota Legislative Council, Committee on Medical Education and Services.

July 1981: "Background Memorandum on the Monitoring of the University of North Dakota's Planning for the Establishment of a Four Year Medical Education Program in North Dakota," North Dakota Legislative Council.

1981: "Report of the North Dakota Legislative Council, Medical Education Committee,."

January 6–March 2, 1981, Legislative Council records, "Minutes of the progress and passage of House Concurrent Resolution HCR3006 Recommending establishment of North Dakota Medical School, third year, in North Dakota."

House and Senate Records

January 29, 1973: Minutes of The Senate Education Committee, re: Senate Bill 2401.

February 5, 1973: Minutes of the Senate Appropriations Committee, re: SB 2401.

February 13, 1973: Journal of the Senate, p. 524.

February 26, 1973: Minutes of the House Education Committee, re: SB 2401.

March 5, 1973: Minutes of the House Appropriations
Committee re: SB 2401.

March 9, 1973: Journal of the House, p. 1221–22.

March, 1973: Forty-third Legislative Assembly of North Dakota:
Senate Bill 2401: "A Bill for an Act expressing the intent
of the forty-third legislative assembly regarding medical
education...."

Transcripts of Interviews Conducted by Dr. Robert Eelkema

December 6, 1978: Interview with Dr. Willard Wright.

November 2, 1994: Interview with Dr. Wally Nelson.

February 23, 1995: Interview with Dr. John Vennes.,

November 21, 1994: Notes of Dr. Robert Eelkema.

Selected Newspaper Articles

"Group to Study, Report on N.D. Medical Crisis," *Grand Forks
Herald,* 12/28/71

"Grant For Establishment of Health Centers Awarded/ Minot Is
Included in Plan," *Minot Daily News,* 9/72.

"Four-Year Medical School," editorial, *Bismarck Tribune,*
11/13/72.

"Education Board to Air Medical Education Plan," *Bismarck
Tribune,* 12/12/72.

'Go Slow' advised for U med school," by Jack Hagerty, *Grand
Forks Herald,* 12/15/72.

"Contract Sought With Minnesota for N.D. Med students," by the
Associated Press, *Fargo Forum,* 12/16/72.

"4-year-school of medicine voted down" by the Associated Press,
Dickinson Press, 12/16/72.

"Medical School delay draws mixed reaction," by Jack Hagerty,
Grand Forks Herald, 12/16/72.

"Angling," by Fischer, *Linton Record*, 12/19/72.

"Minnesota Suggests UND Medical Plans," *Bismarck Tribune*, 12/23/72.

"Action Needed in N.D. on Medical Education," *Fargo Forum* editorial, 12/24/72.

"Editors' Voices: Medical School Report Disappointing," *Minot Daily News*, 1/13/73, attributed to Frank Hornstein editor of *Pierce County Tribune* at Rugby.

"N.D. Medical Education Program Sponsors Said More Optimistic," by the Associated Press, *Fargo Forum*, 1/25/73.

"Governor Signs Medical School Bill, Vetoes Coal Severance Tax," by the Associated Press, *Minot Daily News*, 3/30/73.

Index

after death of husband, 198
on Dunn, Gary, 62
INMED grant and, 170

E
Eelkema, Bob
AHEC budget and, 161–164
AHEC proposal and, 140–143,
161
AHEC staffing and, 168–171
background of, 45–48
on Chuck House Cabinet,
128–130
Dunn and, 64–65, 133
federal grants and, 137,
142–143
Fenderson, Doug, and,
139–140
grant administration by, 171
on Harwood, 102
INMED grant and, 170, 237
Mameluke theory of, 37
MEDEX and, 49–51, 54–59,
138
at Medical Education Com-
mittee meeting,
101–104, 165, 173
at Michigan State seminar,
156–159
in public health department,
48–51
travel by, 69–71
on 2-1-1 plan, 178, 186

on Vennes, John, 103
Wright, Willard, and, 45
Egdahl, Dick, 131
Elder, Bill, 255
Ellendale, North Dakota, indus-
trial school at, 92
Endicott, Kenneth, 138
Epidemic Intelligence Service
(EIS), 220

F
faculty
Clifford on, 31–32
as competition, for doctors,
120
search for, 152–153,
168–171, 197
Fargo, North Dakota
medical practice in, 78
opposition in, 148–151,
174–175, 177–178,
195–196, 224–225,
257
pediatrics in, 223
reputation of, 77–79
feasibility study
under Dunn, 61, 66–67,
104–105, 111–117
Medical Education Commit-
tee on, 89, 91–94,
100–108
necessity for, 58–59
federal grants